CREATING Compelling Conversations

REPRODUCIBLE SEARCH AND SHARE ACTIVITIES FOR ENGLISH TEACHERS

WRITTEN BY:

Eric H. Roth and Teresa X. Nguyen

EDITED BY:

Andrea Schmidt

FOREWORD BY:

Brent Warner

CONTRIBUTORS: *Toni Aberson, Hal Bogotch, Trinity Bustria, Shiggy Ichinomiya, Yuka Kuroda, Tuanni B. Vasconcelos*

CHIMAYO PRESS

©2019

Creating Compelling Conversations:
Reproducible Search and Share Exercises for English Teachers
ISBN-13: 978-1-7326070-0-2 (paperback)

Photographs licensed from Adobe Stock
Cover and book design by Andrea Schmidt

Chimayo Press
12405 Venice Blvd., #424
Los Angeles, CA 90066
United States of America
310-390-0131
855-375-2665

www.ChimayoPress.com
www.CompellingConversations.com

Note: This English teacher's resource book, like all Chimayo Press books, reflects the hard work of several dedicated ESL/EFL teachers. Please respect our work, and avoid using pirated copies of the text. We deeply appreciate your decision to purchase a copy!

To ask questions, share comments, contribute suggestions, or order additional copies, please visit our website, www.ChimayoPress.com, or email eric@compellingconversations.com. Thanks!

In Memory Of
Roy Uriah Aberson
& Doris Stark Aberson

Their endless curiosity and deep knowledge of art, culture, history, and sports continue to inspire. Thank you for showing me many ways to learn, live, and grow.

> "Dream no small dreams for they have no power to move the hearts of men."
> —Johann Wolfgang von Goethe (1749-1832), German poet

Praise from English Teachers

"I first learned of Eric H. Roth when I came across his Compelling Conversations: Questions & Quotations on Timeless Topics several years ago. It quickly became a valuable and much-used resource for my advanced online EFL classes. This latest Search and Share compilation looks to be an equally valuable aid to instructors of highly motivated English students. It combines wide-ranging, outside-the-classroom research activities (Search) – in which students are sent to the Internet or sent outside to explore their community and to engage with native English speakers – with in-class activities (Share) where the students share and discuss the results of their research. The questions asked are both information-based and open-ended, providing ample opportunity for challenging and meaningful conversation practice. Any EFL instructor.... is sure to find Roth's latest work an invaluable resource."

— **Carl W. Hart**, EFL Instructor, author of *Secrets of Teaching ESL Grammar*

"I have been using the Compelling Conversation Series for the last ten years in my college classes. Since then, I have moved on to managing a busy network of private K-12 schools across the world and an online component as well. With the move, I have discovered that the new Compelling Conversation series is perfect for our Middle and High School students. Most other ESL books are not geared towards relevant conversations that encourage students to talk. Our students love the series to the point that the conversations spill over into their breaks and lunchtime."

— **Mark Treston**, Director, Global Innovation Schools; *www.globalinnovationus.com*

"A valuable addition to the classroom. This book encourages students to search and find authentic English material - an invaluable method to get students discovering new and interesting material they may have otherwise missed. The other factor I love about this book is that it offers a framework for students to voice their own opinions, feelings and points of interest. Empowering students to discuss topics and points they themselves find interesting is a sure fire way to improve recall. Great work!"

—**Ben Worthington**, *IELTSpodcast.com*

"Eric Roth's *Creating Compelling Conversations: Reproducible Search and Share Activities for English Teachers* is sure to be a huge hit for language instructors and students alike. The activities that are included in this book are all easy to understand and do, and what I love about them the most is that they make the learning experience personalized, so students can focus on learning what is most important to them. By making the experience relevant to what students want to learn, these activities will ensure that students enjoy learning English and will be excited about their studies, as opposed to more traditional grammar-based studies. It's time for innovation in this industry, and *Creating Compelling Conversations* is spot on."

—**David Stevens**, Director of The Language School; *www.thelanguageschool.us*

FOREWORD: Fresh Materials Bring Fresh Perspectives

English teachers have been encouraging their students for years to take their language learning out of the classroom and into their everyday lives. Teachers know that the best way to truly develop proficiency is through exposure, interaction, and manipulation of language. Unfortunately, too many teachers have left it at the mere suggestion that using language beyond the school is beneficial. Meanwhile, other dedicated English teachers have struggled with finding modern methods and practical materials that motivate students to use English outside academic settings.

For these very reasons, Eric Roth's Search and Share activities have been a favorite of teachers and students using the Compelling Conversations series for years. They provide structured paths for students to customize their language acquisition and development in a way that the students can fully tailor to their own interests. Not only are these activities engaging, they encourage students to search for practical vocabulary and grammatical structures that may go beyond the original scope of the activity. This flexibility allows English students to take ownership of their expanding language skills in an appealing, communicative style – a far cry from the many prescriptive, grammar-first textbooks filled with dated topics. This collection of reproducible worksheets gives students both a choice and a voice.

This ability for students to guide their own learning paths through Search and Share activities hits a lot of the buzzwords in modern teaching: Differentiated Instruction, Formative Assessment, Project-Based Learning, Flipped Classrooms, 4C (Communication, Critical Thinking, Creativity, Collaboration) and more. But beyond the buzzwords, experienced teachers recognize that these activities work because they get students to the joy of learning. Developing linguistic skills becomes less of a task and more of an adventure when you start to unlock the doors of communication through students sharing their own personal experiences and interests.

Fresh materials create fresh perspectives. The Internet provides tons of authentic, contemporary materials for student engagement. Many of these Search and Share activities take advantage of the Internet and social media by exposing students to information and opportunities in new ways, linking their lives and interests in English with classroom assignments.

Allowing (and requiring) English students to select and work with authentic materials has another positive effect. Not only will the English classes be more interesting for the students, but teachers will find each lesson offers new materials and new conversations. We all know some cynical teachers and bored students who feel that there is nothing new under the sun and even less so inside their English classrooms. These creative activities, however, counter those common misperceptions with new materials, engaging questions and lively conversations. Students will hunt for fascinating stories to share, evaluate sources, and bring discoveries from the Internet into small group discussions. In a communicative English class, the more students talk, the more compelling the conversation becomes. By having students co-create these timely lessons, you breathe fresh life into the classroom environment. Let your students search and share!

I hope you enjoy implementing, engaging with, and even altering these communicative activities to the needs of your classroom and your students as much as I have with mine. There is nothing quite as rewarding as watching students take an idea and run with it: welcome to the race!

Brent Warner
Assistant Professor of ESL
Irvine Valley College

How can we create more compelling English classroom conversations? How can we encourage – or reawaken – student curiosity? What can we do to spark more lively discussions in small groups? What materials can keep our English lessons remain current and bring contemporary trends into our classes?

This English Teachers Resource, created by experienced English teachers, is our partial response to those practical questions. The book includes 75+ reproducible worksheets and communicative activities, valuable resources and partial answers.

We believe giving English students more choice and a stronger voice offers authentic opportunities to help students expand their vocabulary, develop speaking skills, and improve their research skills too. These reproducible worksheets and experiences make it easier for hectic teachers to entice students into participating and co-creating positive English language experiences.

How do you flip your English class? What speaking activities do you use to spark lively discussions in small groups? How do you create meaningful small group discussions in your English class?

One effective teaching technique we've often used is called "Search and Share." This communicative internet homework activity encourages - actually requires - English students to take an active role in their English classes. The ESL or EFL students find their own videos and newspaper articles that match their interests, summarize the material, and evaluate its quality. Search and Share also allows students to also share more of their personal interests with classmates in a safe, focused manner on chosen themes.

What is Search and Share?

Over the last decade, we have used Search and Share activities as homework in international high schools, Californian community colleges and American university English classes. The popular activity can be used as a supplemental speaking exercise or extended into an entire class. Because students often want to present compelling material, they will spend far more time reviewing possible videos and potential articles than we would ever require for homework too. Plus, this self-driven research helps students become more familiar with the topics.

English students share the information they have collected (job interview advice, review of a TED talk, favorite charity/non-profit, etc). Then, students break into small groups of 3-5 students at a small table or a circle of chairs. Soon everyone presents their "research," and the other students proceed to ask at least one question each. Each round usually takes 15-20 minutes to finish a search and share in our university classrooms. Community college, high school, and adult classes may differ.

We know – and our students soon discover –authentic sources are not equally credible. Students often develop critical thinking skills by discussing the information they collected in small groups. Why did you choose this source? What was the main idea? What evidence was provided? How strong was the evidence? Who was quoted? What else do we know about this topic? What else would we like to know? Did the article seem fair? Why? How does this match personal experiences?

Small group discussions and focused conversations around student research encourages students to think, reflect, and question sources and information.

Using Search and Share to Improve Speaking Skills

Practice makes progress in conversation skills and discussion activities too. English teachers can also move students into new groupings, and take the communicative activity a few steps further. Students can present their "research" again, but this time they must include all the information that they were asked in the first round. The second telling provides more details. It's also usually clearer and tighter. Once again, however, every student asks every presenter a question. This conversation practice pushes shy students to ask questions and gives all students practice in responding to questions in English.

In a 50-minute class, we usually only have time for two rounds. Yet in an 80-minute class, we usually have time for three rounds and a class discussion. As English teachers, we circle around in different groups, ask questions, and take notes. We usually summarize some "good mistakes" – or common errors – at the end of the activity or class. We also often ask students to post the links to their selected videos or articles on a class website so other students can easily access the recommended materials to keep sharing information. Sometimes English students will be asked to develop a PPT presentation and prepare a class presentation for the following class.

Extension Activities

In writing classes, we often use these worksheets to introduce new topics for movie reviews, research papers, or letters to the editor. We've included bonus final projects for all Search and Share worksheets at the end of each unit. We often choose to only grade this final project. Teachers may want to grade both the process and final product.

Students consistently praise this flexible assignment on their course evaluations. Search and Share exercises first appeared at the end of each chapter in most of the *Compelling Conversations* series. All assignments are easily adaptable for many EFL/ESL classrooms across the globe.

Flexible Contexts

Further, these friendly, communicative exercises work as both independent and supplemental research activities. Although initially designed for advanced English language learners in universities, the thematic worksheets are also useful to high school English and Social Studies teachers. Some sections, such as Exploring New Career Opportunities, also meet the needs of adult and vocational program centers. (English teachers might also find some exercises for relatives and friends!) The dedicated English educators behind this collection of reproducible materials have worked in Brazil, China, France, Japan, Spain, Thailand and Vietnam. We have also taught English in the United States to students from dozens of other countries. These positive classroom experiences give us confidence that these flexible activities and worksheets can appeal to and help English language learners in many distinct situations.

- A Brazilian engineering student can improve their pronunciation and increase clarity in their daily conversations.

- An ambitious Chinese high school student studying English in Shanghai can boost their IELTS and TOEFL scores and research American universities.

- A Mexican immigrant can describe their dream home and discuss their favorite sports game.

- Refugees and Americans by choice can explore American social etiquette and develop their job search skills.

Learning By Doing Research

Richard Feynman, an American physicist and a 1965 Nobel Prize winner, developed a technique for learning for his CalTech research assistants.

1. Pick a topic you want to understand and start studying it.
2. Teach the topic to someone – in clear language.
3. Identify gaps in your knowledge. Fill the gaps.
4. Organize information and simplify. Tell a story.

These same four steps, known as the Feynman Technique of Learning, have become quite popular in physics and science education. Our English students can also use these steps in expanding their English language skills. Our Search and Share activities guide students through a similar learning process.

- Students pick a source on a topic and/or resource. They study it.

- Students teach their classmates about the topic and/or resource in clear language.

- Students, through discussions with classmates, recognize gaps in their knowledge.

- Students, in the extension exercises, organize information and tell a story.

Result? The English students learn by doing research. They also realize they can continually learn, conduct research, and share research both inside and outside their English classrooms. We also hope English students choose to think, reflect, and question more both inside and outside the English classroom.

What will your students learn? What information will they bring into your English classes? How will you use these Search and Share activities in your classes?

> "The person who says he knows what he thinks but cannot express it usually does not know what he thinks."
> –Mortimer J. Adler (1902-2001), American educator and philosopher

CONTENTS

CONTENTS

CONTENTS

CONTENTS

A Studying English

TOPICS:

Getting to Know Each Other: Ice Breakers

Student Name: _____ Date: _____

Let's get to know each other better! Search for a video on YouTube (in English) about icebreaker (or ice breaker) activities and/or questions to start conversations. Then, answer the following questions.

Title: _____

Web address: _____

Author: _____ Length: _____

Publication: _____ Publication date: _____

1 Describe the video you chose. In what context are these people being introduced?

2 Name one icebreaker that was featured in the video you chose.

3 Have you used this icebreaker before? When? Was it useful?

4 What opinions are expressed in the video?

5 What did you learn from watching this video?

6 What was the most interesting part for you? Why?

7 Write five new vocabulary words, idioms, or expressions related to the topic.

   a

   b

   c

   d

   e

8 Why did you choose this video?

9 How would you rate the article on a scale of 1–5, with 5 being the highest? Why?

10 What is your favorite question to start conversations with? Why?

> "Do the best you can, and don't take life too serious."
> —Will Rogers (1879-1935), American actor and humorist

Listening to the Radio and Podcasts to Learn English

Student Name: _____ Date: _____

Do you listen to the radio or podcasts? How can you use the radio and podcasts to improve your listening skills in English? There are hundreds of excellent radio programs from news (BBC, Marketplace, NPR News, Voice of America) to culture shows (ThisAmericanLife, Science Fridays). Please find a radio program that you would like to share with your classmates. Listen to the radio program, find the transcript (text), take notes, and share the program with classmates.

Radio broadcast/podcast title: _____
Web address: _____
Length: _____ Narrator: _____

1. Why did you choose this program?

2. Please describe the radio program or podcast.

3. What was the main idea of the radio broadcast/podcast?

4. What did you learn listening to the segment?

5. How many times did you listen to the broadcast? Why?

6. What was the most interesting part of the radio show or podcast? Why?

7. List and explain five (5) new English vocabulary words you learned from the program.

   a

   b

   c

   d

   e

8. Who do think is the target audience for this program? Why?

9. Who would you recommend this program to? Why?

10. How would you rate the program on a scale of 1–5, with 5 being the highest? Why?

> "In radio, you have two tools. Sound and silence."
> —Ira Glass (1959-), American radio personality and host of "This American Life"

Discussing Dr. Martin Luther King Jr.'s Dream

Student Name: _____ Date: _____

Dr. Martin Luther King, Jr. was an African-American civil rights activist and Baptist minister from Atlanta, Georgia. He promoted social freedom and political equality of all Americans from 1954 to 1968. Dr. King gave a very influential speech called "I Have a Dream" on August 28, 1963 at the Lincoln Memorial in Washington, D.C. This historic speech, delivered before over 200,000 people and millions more on live national television, reviewed a difficult past, a tense present, and a hopeful future for the United States. Please read and listen to Dr. King's "I Have a Dream" speech. Then answer the following questions and discuss with your classmates.

1. What is the context of Dr. King's speech? How do you know?

2. What are some references or allusions to American history that Dr. King makes in his speech?

3. What are some phrases that Dr. King repeats in his speech?

4. Why do you think Dr. King used this rhetorical technique?

5. What are some symbols or metaphors Dr. King uses in his famous speech?

6. Which metaphor or symbol stood out for you? Why?

7. What are some specific examples Dr. King gives in his speech?

8. What are your favorite lines from Dr. King's speech? Why?

9. Write five new vocabulary words, idioms, or expressions found in Dr. King's speech.

    a.

    b.

    c.

    d.

    e.

10. If Dr. King were alive today, what issues do you think he would be working on? Why?

> "The ultimate measure of a man is not where he stands in moments of comfort and convenience, but where he stands at times of challenge and controversy. The true neighbor will risk his position, his prestige, and even his life for the welfare of others."
> —Dr. Martin Luther King (1928-1968), 1964 Nobel Peace Prize winner

Becoming an Independent Reader

Student Name: _____ Date: _____

Demonstrate your knowledge of reading by exploring how you read, what you read, and what you think when you read. Then practice your conversation skills by sharing what you read and discovered.

Share the following with a partner:

- Title and author of the article you read from **DOGO News** or **Business Insider** (link below)
- At **least** ONE answer from the HOW YOU READ column
- At **least** TWO answers from the WHAT YOU READ column
- At **least** ONE answer from the WHAT YOU THINK column

Answer in complete sentences with specific details to support your answer. You may choose which questions to answer.

HOW YOU READ	WHAT YOU READ	WHAT YOU THINK
➤ I was distracted by… ➤ I started to think about… ➤ I got stuck when… ➤ I was confused/focused today because… ➤ One strategy I used to help me read this better was…. ➤ When I got distracted I tried to refocus myself by… ➤ These words or phrases were new/interesting to me…I think they mean…. ➤ When reading I should… ➤ When I read I realized that… ➤ I had a difficult time understanding… ➤ I'll read better next time if I…	➤ Why does the character/ author… ➤ Why doesn't the character/ author… ➤ What surprised me most was… ➤ I predict that… ➤ I noticed that the author uses… ➤ If I could, I'd ask the author… ➤ The most interesting event/ idea in this article is… ➤ I realized… ➤ The main idea in this article is… ➤ I wonder why… ➤ One theme that keeps coming up is… ➤ I found the following quote interesting…. ➤ I _____ this article because…	➤ I think _____ because… ➤ A good example of _____ is… ➤ This reminded me of _____ because… ➤ This was important because… ➤ One thing that surprised me was _____ because I always thought…. ➤ I like the way… ➤ I dislike… ➤ If I were the author, I would… ➤ My favorite part…

> "I cannot live without books; but fewer will suffice
> where amusement, and not use, is the only future object."
> —Thomas Jefferson (1743-1846) 3rd President of the United States

Learning English Through Songs

Student Name: _____ Date: _____

Please find a song in English that you would like to share with your classmates. Listen to the song, find the lyrics, take notes, and share with classmates.

Song title: _____

Web address: _____

Singer: _____ Songwriter: _____

Length: _____ Year released: _____

1 Please describe the song.

2 What makes this song special?

3 What genre of music is the song? What others songs belong to that genre?

4 How many times did you listen to the song? Why?

5 What do you know about the singer?

6 List five (5) new English words or phrases you heard in the song.

    a

    b

    c

    d

    e

7 Who do think this song was written for? Why?

8 Why did you choose this song?

9 Did you find a metaphor in your song? What do you think this metaphor means? Why?

10 How would you rate the song on a scale of 1–5, with 5 being the highest? Why?

> "Much as I adore the melodies, I choose a song for what it has to say."
> —Julie Andrews (1935-) English actress

Finding English Pronunciation Tips on YouTube

Student Name: _____ Date: _____

Find a YouTube video clip that gives tips or suggestions on improving English pronunciation. Look for better ways to make certain sounds (example: 'th' sound in 'that', pronouncing word endings, short vowels). Watch the video, listen carefully, take notes, and share the pronunciation tips with your classmates.

Video title: _____

Web address: _____

Length: _____ Creator: _____

1   What is the video about?

2   What pronunciation tips did the video give?

3   Which words or sounds did the video focus on?

4   Which words or sounds in the video would you most like to work on?

5   What was the strongest part? Why?

6   What was the weakest part? Why? What would you add?

7   Who do you think would be the best audience for this video?

8   What did you learn from this video?

9   Why did you choose this video?

10 How would you rate this video, on a scale of 1–5, with five being the highest? Why?

> "I was the kind nobody thought could make it. I had a funny Boston accent. I couldn't pronounce my R's. I wasn't a beauty."
> —Barbara Walters (1929–), American television journalist

Finding English Pronunciation Tips on YouGlish

Student Name: _____ Date: _____

Do you know **YouGlish.com** yet? Go to the impressive pronunciation site. Put in a word that you have trouble saying clear enough in English. Listen to five different authentic speakers use the word. Read the pronunciation tips listed on website. Now compare that word to a similar, but different word. Repeat this activity for a phrase, an academic term, and a minimum pair (sea/she, sink/think, live/leave). Listen carefully, take notes, and share the pronunciation tips with your classmates.

1. What word did you first choose? Why?

2. What was the first video shown? Who was the speaker?

3. What pronunciation tips did YouGlish.com provide for this word?

4. What were some similar words? List a few.

5. Which word from your list did you choose to compare with the original word?

6. What phrase did you choose? Why?

7. What academic term or specialized word did you choose? Why?

8. Which minimal pair did you choose? Why?

9. What pronunciation tips did you learn?

10. How can you use YouGlish.com to improve your pronunciation?

"The bold adventurer succeeds the best."
– Ovid (43 B.C.E. – 17 C.E.), Roman poet

 **Search & Share**

Reviewing Stress Patterns in English

Student Name: _____ Date: _____

Find a video that gives tips or suggestions on common word stress patterns in English. Stress patterns are very important in improving your pronunciation of English words and sentences. Better understanding stress patterns in English will help you be better understood as an English speaker. Watch the video, listen carefully, take notes, and share the pronunciation tips with your classmates.

Video title: _____

Web address: _____

Length: _____ Creator: _____

1   Describe the video.

2   What pronunciation tips did the selected video give?

3   Which individual words or sounds did the video focus on?

4   What was the strongest part? Why?

5   What was the weakest part? Why?

6   Who do you think is the target audience for this video?

7   Does your best language use stress? How?

8   Do you think this video will help improve your pronunciation of English words and sentences? Were you able to reproduce the same sound?

9   How would you rate this video, on a scale of 1–5, with five being the highest? Why?

10   What are some other English words where you have noticed that stress matters?

> **"We learn by doing."**
> – English proverb

Mirroring: A Pronunciation Technique

Student Name: _____ Date: _____

A technique called mirroring can improve your speech and your ability to monitor your pronunciation. The goal is to study a native English speaker on video and copy the speaker's words and gestures as you see and hear them. This will help you sound and look more like a native speaker.

1. Choose a model.
   a. This should be an American person whom you admire and want to imitate
      [e.g. Dr. Martin Luther King Jr., Steve Jobs, Lady Gaga, Barack Obama...]
   b. Find a video of this American native English speaker
      [e.g. Youtube, TEDtalk, etc.]. The speaker should be speaking for at least 3-5 minutes.

2. Analyze the speaker and the speech.
   a. Study the video of this speaker as many times as you need to complete the assignment.
   b. Focus on a particular sound or gesture.
   c. Record 5 sentences that you find effective and focus on a keyword or gesture.
   d. Play the video and mirror the speaker while watching the selected sentences.

3. Present your findings.
   You can include:
   a. Information about the speaker and how the video can be found (e.g. website address).
   b. A brief introduction about why you chose this speaker.
   c. A conclusion about the particular way that your speaker talks. Does he use a lot of hand gestures? Does he make certain mouth movements or facial expressions when speaking? Does he pause a lot or repeat certain words frequently?

When presenting, play the video and then mirror 1-2 minutes of the speaker you chose. Try to copy everything the speaker says a few seconds after you hear it. Imitate the speaker's hand, face and body movements. Notice how the movements go with the speech. You will have to practice this many times for it to get easier. The more times you repeat the mirroring, the more it will help you.

Have fun and enjoy!

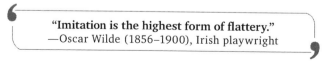

"Imitation is the highest form of flattery."
—Oscar Wilde (1856–1900), Irish playwright

1. GETTING TO KNOW EACH OTHER: ICE BREAKERS (PG. 2)

Can you introduce yourself to your classmates? Create a 60 to 90-second video introduction for your peers. Please include your name, two things that you like, a favorite movie, a favorite song, and a favorite dish/meal. Finally, let us know two things that you want to learn this year.

2. LISTENING TO THE RADIO AND PODCASTS TO LEARN ENGLISH (PG. 3)

What news from your country would you like to share? Record a two to three-minute video of yourself reporting on news from your country. Share your video and transcript on the class blog.

3. DISCUSSING DR. MARTIN LUTHER KING JR.'S DREAM (PG. 4)

What would Dr. King be doing if he were alive today? Select one issue that you believe Dr. King would work on today if he were alive. Then create a 2-4 minute video explaining why Dr. King would address that topic. Share your video on the class blog.

4. BECOMING AN INDEPENDENT READER (PG. 5)

What did you read? What did you think about the article? Summarize the article and share your opinion of the topic in a few focused paragraphs.

5. LEARNING ENGLISH THROUGH SONGS (PG. 6)

What are your favorite English language singers and songs? Choose a partner or form a group of least three people. Give a video review of a favorite singer, group, song, or album in a 3-4 minute video and upload it to the class blog. Remember to cite sources and give credit where credit is due.

6. FINDING ENGLISH PRONUNCIATION TIPS ON YOUTUBE (PG. 7)

Can you think of any English words that sound alike? Pick two or three words that are similar to each other that you sometimes have a hard time pronouncing. After practicing the pronunciation tips which you have examined, create a 60 to 90-second video of yourself using those tips. Send your video to your English teacher for feedback.

7. REVIEWING PRONUNCIATION TIPS ON YOUGLISH (PG. 8)

a) What are some important English words in your field or major? Watch 3 clips from YouGlish featuring the word. Select one to explain to your classmates in a 60 to 90-second video. Send your video to your instructor for feedback.

b) What other minimal pairs (ex: sat vs. sit, buy vs. boy, trip vs. tip) can you think of? Choose a minimal pair you sometimes have trouble pronouncing. Make a 60 to 90-second video of yourself using the pronunciation tips you discovered on YouGlish with these minimal pairs. Send your video to your instructor for feedback.

8. REVIEWING STRESS PATTERNS IN ENGLISH (PG. 9)

What English words require proper stress? Select three words with stress patterns that you have trouble pronouncing. After practicing the pronunciation tips you've assessed, create a 60 to 90-second video of yourself using each of the three words a sentence. Make sure to speak as clearly as possible so listeners can understand you. Send your video to your instructor for feedback.

9. MIRRORING: A PRONUNCIATION TECHNIQUE (PG. 10)

What can you learn from imitating the speaking patterns and gestures of another person? Make a video of yourself mirroring the speaker from the video you watched. Copy everything the speaker says and imitate his/her speech, expressions and body language. Upload your video to the class blog and have fun!

B Preparing for College Life

TOPICS:

Collecting Academic Advice on the Internet

Student Name: _____ Date: _____

Find a video online that provides tips for success in school or college. The video might suggest ways to improve test scores, get better grades, choose a college, overcome procrastination, or some other aspect of succeeding in school. Watch the video, take notes, and review the video for your classmates.

Video title: _____

Web address: _____

Length: _____ Creator: _____

1. Describe the video.

2. What tips did the video provide?

3. What was the most important idea? Why?

4. Where do you think the video was produced? Why?

5. How practical did you find the advice? Why?

6. What was the strongest part? Why?

7. What was the weakest part? Why?

8. Do you think any important information is missing? What else would you like to know on this topic?

9. Why did you choose this video?

10. What does academic success mean to you? Why?

> "Education is learning what you didn't even know you didn't know."
> —Daniel J. Boorstin (1914–2004), American historian

College Expectations

Student Name: ———————————————————— Date: ————————————————

As a new college student, you can learn a lot from your peers and upperclassmen about campus life. Find out more about your college/university by interviewing at least 3 fellow students.

1. Ask them what tips they have for you, as a new student to the college.
2. Ask them what professors expect of a college student.
3. What are your responsibilities as a college student?
4. Then, create at least one more question that you may be interested in finding out.

This is a total of at least 4 questions for at least 3 college students. Write what you've learned.

Questions:	Student #1: ———	Student #2: ———	Student #3: ———	Extra Notes

> **"Do not be afraid to ask for help. Nobody gets through college on their own."**
> —Michelle Obama (1964 -), American lawyer and former First Lady of the United States

Choosing an American University

Student Name: _____ Date: _____

Choosing where to pursue your desired degree or education program can be a tough decision to make. Sometimes it helps to make a list or chart to compare your options. For this exercise, choose two (2) American universities you are interested in attending and do some research on each school. Then, fill out the chart below and compare your findings.

Questions:	Choice #1:	Choice #2:
What is the name of this university?		
Which major offered at this university interests you the most?		
Is the school located in a big city or a "college town"? What's the surrounding area like?		
Is student housing offered at each university? Is it on or off-campus?		
What is the cost of tuition per semester?		
What extracurricular activities and clubs are offered on-campus? Are there fraternities/sororities?		
Name three (3) advantages of attending this university.		
Name three (3) disadvantages of attending this university.		
Based on the research you've done, which American school seems like the better fit for you? Why?		

"An investment in knowledge pays the best interest."
—Benjamin Franklin (1706-1790) American author and statesman

Navigating an American Classroom

Student Name: _____ Date: _____

Interview a native English speaking student about his/her American classroom knowledge and experiences. Write as many details as possible when answering so that you can share with classmates. Remember to use complete sentences.

Start by asking: What do you do…

1 When you first walk into class?

2 If you have a question in class?

3 If you know the answer to a question in class?

4 If you need to use the restroom during class?

5 If you are tired in class?

6 If you don't like the class activity?

7 If you don't understand something a teacher says?

8 If another student is bothering you?

9 When you leave class?

10 If you're struggling with the homework assignment?

BONUS: Do you think that teachers should ban the use of smartphones in class? Why?

> "The classroom should be an entrance into the world, not an escape from it."
> —John Ciardi (1916-1986), American poet and translator

Preparing for the IELTS - Speaking Section

Student Name: _____ Date: _____

What do you know about the speaking section of the International English Language Testing System (IELTS)? Search for a video that describes and gives advice on the speaking section of the IELTS exam. Afterwards, answer the following questions and share them with your peers.

Title: _____

Web address: _____

Author: _____ Length: _____

Publication: _____ Publication date: _____

1 Describe the video you selected.

2 How does the video describe the IELTS speaking section?

3 Why do you think the speaking section is challenging for some students?

4 List three (3) important strategies for the speaking section of the IELTS exam discussed in the video.

    a

    b

    c

5 What did you like the most about the video?

6 What did you learn from the video that you did not know before?

7 Write five new vocabulary words, idioms, or expressions related to the topic.

    a

    b

    c

    d

    e

8 If you could give one piece of advice to your classmates about the IELTS speaking section, what would you say?

9 On a scale of 1-5, how would you rate this video for IELTS test takers? Why?

10 Where would you like to speak English better? Why?

> **"Speak your mind, even if your voice shakes."**
> —Maggie Smith (1934-), English actress

Preparing for the IELTS - Writing Section

Student Name: _____ Date: _____

What do you know about the writing section of the International English Language Testing System (IELTS)? Search for an article that describes and gives advice on the writing section of the IELTS exam. Afterwards, answer the following questions and share them with your peers.

Title: _____
Web address: _____
Author: _____ Length: _____
Publication: _____ Publication date: _____

1 Describe the article you selected.

2 How does the article describe the IELTS writing section?

3 Why do you think the writing section is challenging for some students?

4 List three (3) important strategies for the writing section of the IELTS exam discussed in the article.

   a
   b
   c

5 What did you like the most about the article?

6 Do you feel more prepared for the test after reading this article? Why or why not?

7 Write five new vocabulary words, idioms, or expressions related to the topic.

   a
   b
   c
   d
   e

8 If you could give one piece of advice to your classmates about the IELTS writing section, what would you say?

9 On a scale of 1-5, how would you rate this article for IELTS test takers? Why?

10 How would being a strong writer make college easier?

> "I can shake off everything as I write; my sorrows disappear, my courage is reborn."
> —Anne Frank (1929-1945), German diarist

Preparing for the SAT - Writing Section

Student Name: _____ Date: _____

What do you know about the writing section of the SAT? Search for an article that describes and gives advice on the writing section of the SAT. Afterwards, answer the following questions and share them with your peers.

Title: _____

Web address: _____

Author: _____ Length: _____

Publication: _____ Publication date: _____

1 Describe the article you selected.

2 How does the article describe the SAT writing section?

3 Why do you think the writing section is challenging for some students?

4 List three (3) important strategies for the writing section of the SAT exam discussed in the article.

    a

    b

    c

5 What did you like the most about the article?

6 What did you learn from the article that you did not know before?

7 Write five new vocabulary words, idioms, or expressions related to the topic.

    a

    b

    c

    d

    e

8 If you could give one piece of advice to your classmates about the SAT writing section, what would you say?

9 On a scale of 1-5, how would you rate this article for SAT test takers? Why?

10 What are some situations where writing clearly or persuasively in English would be helpful?

> "Sometimes, the most brilliant and intelligent minds do not shine in standardized tests because they do not have standardized minds."
> —Diane Ravitch (1938-), professor and education historian

Preparing for the TOEFL - Speaking Section

Student Name: _____ Date: _____

What do you know about the speaking section of the Test of English as a Foreign Language (TOEFL)? To better prepare, search for a video on the topic that summarizes and gives advice on taking the exam. Then, answer the following questions and review with your classmates in small group discussions:

Title: _____

Web address: _____

Author: _____ Length: _____

Publication: _____ Publication date: _____

1 Describe the video you selected.

2 How does the video describe the TOEFL speaking section?

3 Why do you think the speaking section is challenging for some students?

4 List three (3) important strategies for the speaking section of the TOEFL exam discussed in the video.

    a

    b

    c

5 What did you like the most about the video?

6 Do you feel more prepared for the test after watching this video? Why or why not?

7 Write five new vocabulary words, idioms, or expressions related to the topic.

    a

    b

    c

    d

    e

8 If you could give one piece of advice to your classmates about the TOEFL speaking section, what would you say?

9 How are English speaking skills important in American universities?

10 On a scale of 1-5, how would you rate this video for TOEFL test takers? Why?

> "To speak and to speak well, are two things. A fool may talk, but a wise man speaks."
> —Ben Jonson (1572-1637), English poet

Preparing for the TOEFL - Writing Section

Student Name: _____ Date: _____

What do you know about the writing section of the Test of English as a Foreign Language (TOEFL)? Search for an article that describes and gives advice on the writing section of TOEFL. Afterwards, answer the following questions and share them with your peers.

Title: _____

Web address: _____

Author: _____ Length: _____

Publication: _____ Publication date: _____

1 Describe the article you selected.

2 How does the article describe the TOEFL writing section?

3 Why do you think the writing section is challenging for some students?

4 List three (3) important strategies for the writing section of the TOEFL exam discussed in the article.

  a

  b

  c

5 What did you like the most about the article?

6 What did you learn from the article that you did not know before?

7 Write five new vocabulary words, idioms, or expressions related to the topic.

  a

  b

  c

  d

  e

8 Do you feel more prepared for the test after reading this article? Why or why not?

9 If you could give one piece of advice to your classmates about the TOEFL writing section, what would you say?

10 On a scale of 1-5, how would you rate this article for TOEFL test takers? Why?

> **"Writing, to me, is simply thinking through my fingers."**
> —Isaac Asimov (1920-1992), American writer and scientist

Understanding Plagiarism

Student Name: _____ Date: _____

What do you know about plagiarism? How is it seen in your country? Plagiarism is a common educational concern, and many English teachers stress the importance of understanding how to use/reference another's work appropriately. Search for a recent article or brochure that describes and discusses plagiarism. After, answer the following questions:

Title: _____
Web address: _____
Author: _____ Length: _____
Publication: _____ Publication date: _____

1   How does the article/brochure describe plagiarism?

2   What is the author's opinion about plagiarism?

3   According to the article, what are three (3) practices considered to be plagiarism?

   a

   b

   c

4   According to the article, what are three (3) ways one can avoid plagiarism?

   a

   b

   c

5   Based on what you read, when is it considered plagiarism to use someone's ideas? Why?

6   What did you learn from the article that you did not know before?

7   In your opinion, is it possible to plagiarize unintentionally? Why or why not?

8   How would you feel if someone plagiarized your work? Why?

9   Do you think plagiarism is a major problem? How widespread do you think is is in your school?

10   How would you rate the article/brochure on a scale of 1–5, with 5 being the highest? Why?

> **'Fine words! I wonder where you stole them?'**
> —Jonathan Swift (1667–1745) - Anglo-Irish satirist and essayist

Extension Activities

1. COLLECTING ACADEMIC ADVICE ON THE INTERNET (PG. 14)

What does academic success look like to you? Write a 300 to 500 word essay describing your definition of academic success. Give examples.

2. COLLEGE EXPECTATIONS (PG. 15)

What is college life on your campus like? Create a three to four-minute video describing what life is like on your campus. Upload your video to the class blog.

3. CHOOSING AN AMERICAN UNIVERSITY (PG. 16)

Which American university would you prefer to go to? Write a 300-500 word essay comparing two of the universities that you selected.

4. NAVIGATING AN AMERICAN CLASSROOM (PG. 17)

a. What is the role of smartphones in the English classroom? Should teachers prohibit the use of smartphones in class? Write a memo to the department head giving your suggestions and reasoning for them.

b. How should one act in an American classroom? Make a three to four-minute video offering advice to a new international student in your school. Be as specific as possibe. Upload your video to the class blog and help others!

5. PREPARING FOR THE IELTS - SPEAKING SECTION (PG. 18)

What are some important strategies and advice key to succeeding on the IELTS speaking unit? Create a two to three-minute video explaining three important strategies and one piece of advice for the speaking unit of the IELTS exam. Share your video on the class blog and help other English language learners!

6. PREPARING FOR THE IELTS - WRITING SECTION (PG. 19)

What are some important strategies to succeeding on the IELTS writing section? Write a short essay explaining three important strategies and one piece of advice for the writing unit of the IELTS exam. Share your advice on the class blog and help other English language learners!

7. PREPARING FOR THE SAT - WRITING SECTION (PG. 20)

What are some important strategies to succeeding on the writing section of the SAT? Write an email to a classmate on how to reach their target score on the SAT. Share your email on the class blog and help other students.

8. PREPARING FOR THE TOEFL - SPEAKING SECTION (PG. 21)

What is some practical advice key to succeeding on the TOEFL speaking section? Create a two to three-minute video explaining three important strategies and one piece of advice for the TOEFL speaking unit. Share your video on the class blog and assist other English language learners!

9. PREPARING FOR THE TOEFL - WRITING SECTION (PG. 22)

What is some practical advice key to succeeding on the TOEFL writing section? Compose an essay with practiced advice for the TOEFL writing unit. Upload your essay to the class blog and help other English language learners!

10. UNDERSTANDING PLAGIARISM (PG. 23)

How can one avoid plagiarism? Create a handout explaining what plagiarism is and how to avoid it. Cite at least three sources.

Creating a Home

TOPICS:

Designing My Dream Home

Student Name: _____ Date: _____

What does your dream home look like? Use your imagination, knowledge, and research to describe your ideal home. Use the vocabulary learned in this lesson. Imagine the possibilities. Dream big!

Location: _____

1 What does the outside of your dream home look like? Do you have a yard? A garden?

2 What kind of neighborhood would you like to live in?

3 How many rooms are there in your dream home?

4 Describe the kitchen:

5 Describe the living room:

6 Describe another room:

7 How do you plan on decorating your dream home?

8 What else makes this home special?

9 What other information or details can you share?

10 Who do you want to live with you in your dream home? Why?

> "Determine what sort of a house will be fit for you; determine to work for it; and to get one that you can entirely enjoy and manage."
> —John Ruskin (1819-1900), English critic

Searching for My Dream Vacation Home: Airbnb

Student Name: _____ Date: _____

Where is your dream vacation home? First, go to **airbnb.com** and choose your dream vacation destination. Second, search for your dream vacation home. How many bedrooms? How many bathrooms? Does it have a view? Describe your dream vacation home. Use the vocabulary you learned in this lesson —and your imagination!

Destination: _____

1. What does the outside of your dream vacation home look like?

2. How would you describe the area? (Search Google Maps for the neighborhood.)

3. What does the inside of your dream vacation home look like?

4. Describe your favorite room.

5. How is your favorite room decorated?

6. What else makes this home special?

7. What activities will you do on this vacation?

8. What other information can you share about your fantasy vacation?

9. Who will stay with you in your dream vacation home? Why?

10. What five adjectives describe your dream vacation home?

> "There is a role and function for beauty in our time."
> —Tadao Ando (1941-), Japanese architect

 **Search & Share**

Reproducible

Talking About Love

Student Name: _____ Date: _____

Are you single? Do you have a partner? Dating is always a complicated topic, but some people like to share ideas and advice on romantic relationships. Search for a YouTube Channel that talks about relationships and do some research on it. Then, select a short video from this channel, watch it, and answer the questions below.

Title: _____
Web address: _____
Author: _____ Length: _____
Publication: _____ Publication date: _____

1 Which YouTube channel did you choose? Describe it.

2 Who created it? What did you find out about this person and their channel?

3 What are the main topics addressed in the videos? Which of them interests you?

4 What do you like about this channel? Why did you choose it instead of another channel?

5 Now let's talk about the video you selected. What is the video about? Summarize.

6 Write five new vocabulary words, idioms, or expressions related to the topic.

   a

   b

   c

   d

   e

7 Which ideas from the video do you agree with? Why?

8 Which ideas from the video do you disagree with? Why?

9 Do you have some suggestions on how to improve this channel?

10 What do you think is the key to a loving relationship?

> "And if my heart be scarred and burned, the safer, I, for all I learned."
> —Dorothy Parker (1893-1967), American poet and satirist

Parenting Today

Student Name: _____ Date: _____

Are you a parent? Do you want to become a parent? Having and raising a child is a topic that comes up at some point. Parenting also involves many big decisions. What would you like to find out about parenting? Search for an article that discusses parenting and answer the following questions. Feel free to share your personal experiences and opinions!

Title: _____

Web address: _____

Author: _____ Length: _____

Publication: _____ Publication date: _____

1 Explain the main idea of the article you selected.

2 According to the article, what is one (1) good aspect of being a parent?

3 According to the article, how can raising a child be challenging?

4 Write five new vocabulary words, idioms, or expressions related to the topic.

a

b

c

d

e

5 Which part of the article do you agree with most? Why?

6 Which part of the article do you disagree with most? Why?

7 Choose one quote from the article that represents your thoughts.

8 How could this article be better? Would adding another source help? How?

9 How would you rate the article on a scale of 1–5, with 5 being the highest? Why?

10 What do you think is the key to a happy, healthy parent-child relationship?

> **With every word we utter, with every action we take, we know our kids are watching us. We as parents are their most important role models.**
> —Michelle Obama (1964 -), American lawyer and former First Lady of the United States

Appreciating Pets

Student Name: _____ Date: _____

Do you have pets? What makes a good pet? What makes a good pet owner? Search for an informative article about caring for pets. After that, please answer the questions below:

Title: _____

Web address: _____

Author: _____ Length: _____

Publication: _____ Publication date: _____

1. Provide a brief summary of the article you chose. What was the main idea?

2. Why did you choose this article?

3. What is the author's opinion on pets?

4. Which ideas from the article/video do you agree with? Why?

5. Identify five verbs in the article.

   a

   b

   c

   d

   e

6. What do you like the most about the article?

7. How could the article be improved?

8. How would you rate the article on a scale of 1–5, with 5 being the highest? Why?

9. What do you look for in pets?

10. What advice can you share with a new pet owner?

> "Dogs are our link to paradise. They don't know evil or jealousy or discontent."
> —Milan Kundera (1929-today) – Czech-born French writer

The Cat's Out of the Bag!

Student Name: _____ Date: _____

Do you like cats? How many types of cats or felines can you think of? Fédération Internationale Féline (FIFe) recognizes 49 breeds of cats. In addition, the National Geographic Blog identifies 38 known species of wild cats. Search online and find out everything you can about one type of cat. Share your findings by answering the following questions:

Title: _____

Web address: _____

Author: _____ Length: _____

Publication: _____ Publication date: _____

1   Which cat or feline did you choose?

2   Have you seen this cat in person? Where? When?

3   What kind of food does this specific feline like to eat? Describe it.

4   What do you find most intersting about this cat?

5   What did you learn about this cat that you did not know before?

6   Write five adjectives in the article.

    a

    b

    c

    d

    e

7   Why did you choose this type of feline?

8   Would you keep this type of cat at home? Why or why not?

9   How would you rate the article/video on a scale of 1–5, with 5 being the highest? Why?

10   What's your favorite type of cat? Why?

> "When a man loves cats, I am his friend and comrade, without further introduction."
> —Mark Twain (1835-1910), American writer and humorist

This I Believe

Student Name: _____ Date: _____

Please select one radio segment from the popular NPR series 'This I Believe.' Find a story that is based on a personal essay, and read by a writer. Choose one that resonates with you. Then listen carefully, take notes, and fill out the worksheet below.

Title: _____

Author/Reader: _____

Length: _____ Date: _____

1. Who is the author? Briefly describe them.

2. What's the main idea shared in the segment?

3. Which part was the most interesting or relatable for you? Why?

4. What was the most surprising thing shared in the segment?

5. Do you agree or disagree with the author's point of view? Why?

6. Write five new vocabulary words, idioms, or expressions related to the topic.

   a.

   b.

   c.

   d.

   e.

7. Why did you choose this story?

8. How effective was this essay on a scale of 1-5, with 5 being the highest? Why?

9. Who do you think is the audience for this podcast? Why?

10. Would you share this essay with a friend? Why or why not?

> "We will not be driven by fear into an age of unreason, if we dig deep in our history and our doctrine, and remember that we are not descended from fearful men – not from men who feared to write, to speak, to associate, and to defend causes that were, for the moment, unpopular."
> —Edward R. Murrow (1908-1965), American broadcast journalist and correspondant

Exploring New Holidays

Student Name: _____ Date: _____

Search on the Internet for a video in English about a holiday or celebration that you do not currently celebrate but that you would like to know more about. Find an article, read it, print it, and discuss it with classmates. You may use **Wikipedia.org** for this assignment. Note: Wikipedia, an open source, free online encyclopedia, can be a good place to <u>start</u> a research project.

Title: _____
Web address: _____
Author: _____ Date: _____

1. Describe the video.

2. What tips did the video provide?

3. What was the most important idea? Why?

4. How practical did you find the advice? Why?

5. What was the strongest part? Why?

6. What questions would you like to ask someone who celebrates this holiday?

7. Why did you choose this video?

8. How would you rate the video on a scale of 1–5, with 5 being the highest? Why?

9. What are some other social, religious, or national holidays?

10. What is your favorite holiday? Why?

> **"Thanksgiving Day is the one day that is truly American."**
> —O. Henry (1862–1910), American short story writer

Celebrating Birthdays

Student Name: _____ Date: _____

Everyone has a birthday. The day you came into this world marked a significant change for those around you.

Do you know what the world was like the day you were born? Do you know how life changed for your family that day? Conduct an Internet search and talk to a relative to find out what life was like when you were born. Take notes and answer the following questions. Discuss your findings with your classmates.

1. Where were you born? Describe the place where you were born.

2. Who was present at your birth?

3. What were some surprises surrounding your birth?

4. What was happening in the world when you were born? What were some major news stories at this time?

5. What songs were popular when you were born?

6. What were some popular movies that year?

7. Who are some famous people who share your birthday?

8. Who do you typically celebrate your birthday with? Why?

9. Do you have any special plans to celebrate your next birthday? Why?

10. What has been the best year of your life so far? Why?

> **"The more you praise and celebrate your life, the more there is in life to celebrate."**
> —Oprah Winfrey (1954–), American star and philanthropist

Becoming Yourself

Student Name: _____ Date: _____

Who are you? What do you like about yourself? The mass media often reinforces the idea that we should be ourselves in entertainment and school. Find a video about staying true to yourself on YouTube or Vimeo and answer the following questions.

1. What is the video or series segment about?

2. Can you describe one or two of the people or characters?

3. How did this person or character express themselves? What made them unique?

4. Did the main person or character face a problem? What was it?

5. What was the main idea of the video?

6. What was the most interesting part for you? Why?

7. Write five vocabulary words related to personality or character.
   a.
   b.
   c.
   d.
   e.

8. Do you think "being yourself" is always a good idea? Why? Why not?

9. Have you ever tried to be like someone else? How did it feel?

10. What are three things that you like about yourself? Why?
    a.
    b.
    c.

> **To thine own self be true, and it must follow, as the night the day, thou canst not then be false to any man.**
> —William Shakespeare (1564–1616), English playwright

1. DESIGNING MY DREAM HOME (PG. 27)

What does your dream home look like? Show us by creating a collage or poster board presentation of what you want your dream home to look like. Use pictures from magazines, catalogs, and the Internet. Prepare to explain your collage in a short presentation.

2. SEARCHING FOR MY DREAM VACATION HOME: AIRBNB (PG. 28)

What does your dream vacatio home look like? Find an ideal vacation home and create a Power-Point presentation describing it. Be prepared to share your presentation with your classmates.

3. TALKING ABOUT LOVE (PG. 29)

How can couples maintain healthy relationships? What is key to a loving relationship? Write an advice column for the school/local paper giving relationship advice. Share your best ideas on keeping a relationship healthy and loving.

4. PARENTING TODAY (PG. 30)

What are some of the challenges in being a parent? What is the key to a happy, healthy parent-child relationship? Compose a 300-500 word advice article on parenting. Discuss the challenges of parenting and what parents can do to form happy, healthy parent-child relationships. Share your thoughts on the class blog.

5. LOVING PETS (PG. 31)

What is some helpful, sound advice on pet ownership? Compose a 300-500-word advice article about owning pets. Upload your article to the class blog and share your insights.

6. THE CAT'S OUT OF THE BAG! (PG. 32)

What do you know about cats? Compose a 300 to 500 word article about a cat breed you researched. Give advice on being a cat owner and upload your article on the class blog.

7. THIS I BELIEVE (PG. 33)

What do you believe? Write an essay explaining your personal philosophy. Consider sharing your essay on the website **ThisIBelieve.org.**

What do you believe? Give a short 4 to 5-minute presentation explaining your personal philosophy. Consider recording your presentation and sharing it online.

8. EXPLORING NEW HOLIDAYS (PG. 34)

Which holiday did you research? Continue your research and introduce it in a brief report with at least 3 sources. Include – and cite – a picture.

9. CELEBRATING BIRTHDAYS (PG. 35)

What was life like the week you were born? Interview a family member about the week you entered the world. Write a letter summarizing your interview to another relative.

10. BECOMING YOURSELF (PG. 36)

What do you like about your life? Write a journal entry listing five positive memories and three positive traits you possess. You can keep this journal private or share with a friend or relative.

Modern Living

TOPICS:

Appreciating Your Style

Student Name: _____ Date: _____

What are some fashion trends today? How have fashions changed over the decades and centuries? Search the web for an article (in English) about a current trend in clothing or fashion. Find an article, read it, print it out, and be prepared to discuss it with classmates.

Title: _____

Author: _____ Length: _____

Publication: _____ Publication date: _____

1   Which clothing or fashion trend is described in your article?

2   How many sources were quoted?

3   Were there any photos or illustrations? What kind?

4   What do you like most about this style? The colors? Fabric? Shapes?

5   Where would you wear these clothes? Why?

6   What did you learn from this article?

7   What was the most interesting part for you? Why?

8   Write five vocabulary words, idioms, or expressions used in the article.

   a
   b
   c
   d
   e

9   How would you rate the article on a scale of 1–5, with 5 being the highest? Why?

10 How would you describe your style?

> "Fashion is about exploring different selves."
> —Jane Fonda (1937–), actress and former fashion model

Exploring American Social Etiquette

Student Name: _____ Date: _____

Every social group has a different code of behavior. America is no different. To better acquaint you with the proper social etiquette in America, research the following questions. In addition to internet research, consider asking friends and family members familiar with American social customs as well!

1   How do you greet someone you have just met?

2   Is it polite to stand when someone enters a room?

3   After how many rings should you answer the phone?

4   When leaving a phone message for someone, what information should you include?

5   When you receive an invitation that requests an RSVP, what does that mean?

6   When is it considered polite to send a thank-you note?

7   At a business lunch, who should pay for the meal?

8   When do you leave tips? How much do you leave?

9   When the National Anthem is being played, where should you be facing?

10 How should you dress for a wedding? What are some popular wedding gifts?

> "The most exhausting thing in life, I have discovered, is being insincere."
> —Anne Morrow Lindbergh (1906-2001), American author

Handling Culture Shock

Student Name: _____ Date: _____

Culture shock occurs when a person feels disoriented in an new environment because they are unfamiliar with the local lifestyle and customs. It's a common experience for immigrants, international students, tourists and ex-pats alike! Choose a video about culture shock online, watch and take notes. Then answer the following questions.

1 How does the video you chose describe culture shock?

2 Is there more than one kind of culture shock? Explain.

3 According to the video, how long does culture shock typically last?

4 List five tips for overcoming culture shock provided in the video.

   a
   b
   c
   d
   e

5 What do you appreciate about being in the United States?

6 What do you find uncomfortable about American culture?

7 What are some ways that American culture is different from yours?

8 How would you rate the video on a scale of 1–5, with 5 being the highest? Why?

9 Have you experienced culture shock? In what ways?

10 What advice would you offer an international student coming to the U.S. for a year?

> "Coming back to America was, for me, much more of a cultural shock than going to India."
> —Steve Jobs (1955-2011), American entrepreneur and Apple co-founder

Reducing Stress and Increasing Happiness

Student Name: _____ Date: _____

We live in stressful times. How can we reduce our stress? How can we increase our happiness?

A. Take the following five-minute online quiz: "True Happiness Compass."
Answer the questions, read your evaluation, and be prepared to discuss stress management tips with your classmates.

1 What did you think of the quiz? How many questions were asked?

2 Can you recall two of the questions from the quiz?

3 How would you rate the online quiz, on a scale of 1–5, with five being the highest? Why?

B. Find a recent article about how to cope with stress and increase happiness.

Title: _____ Publication/Website: _____
Author: _____ Publication Date: _____

1 What's the main idea?

2 How many sources were quoted?

3 How reliable were the sources quoted? Why?

4 What was the strongest part of the article? Why?

5 How would you rate the article on a scale of 1–5, with five being the highest? Why?

BONUS: What are your best tips for a happy, healthy life?

> "For fast acting relief, try slowing down."
> —Lilly Tomlin (1939–), American comedian

Examining a TED Talk

Student Name: _____ Date: _____

Have you heard about TED (Technology, Entertainment, and Design) talks yet? These "riveting talks by remarkable people" according to TED.com, come from global experts in many disciplines. The presenters give personal presentations that address many important, entertaining topics in short, engaging talks. Themes range from culture, science, and happiness to business, education, and technology. Find a short video on a topic of particular interest to you. Watch and listen to the talk two times before answering the following questions. Finally, be prepared to review the TED talk for your classmates in small group discussions.

Video title: _____

Length: _____ Speaker: _____

Date: _____ Location: _____

1 What is the speaker's background?

2 Who was the audience?

3 How did the speaker begin the presentation?

4 What is the theme of the talk? Does it match the title? How?

5 What was a memorable part of this TED talk? What made it memorable?

6 How did the speaker connect to the audience? (Humor, visual aids, etc.)

7 What did the speaker want to accomplish? Do you think the speaker achieved their goals?

8 Did the speaker convince you? Why or why not?

9 Why did you choose this TED talk?

10 How would you rate this TED talk on a scale of 1–5, with five being the highest? Why?

> "We only think when confronted with a problem."
> — John Dewey (1859- 1952), American philosopher and educational reformer

Taking Public Transportation

Student Name: ———————————————— Date: ————————————

How do you move from one place to another in your city? Do you use public transportation? How? Why?

Public transportation is a system of buses, trains, subways, trams, roads, walkways, bike lanes, etc to help people get around. Please find a short, interesting article (500-1000 words) in English about some public transportation news. It might be a new project, an old station, or a recent controversy. Read the article, summarize it, and be prepared to discuss it.

Title: ———————————————————————————————
Author: ————————————————— Length: ———————————
Publication: ————————————— Publication date: ——————————

1. What's the article's main idea?

2. How many sources were quoted? Who is quoted?

3. Was there a quote that stood out to you? Why?

4. What did you learn from the article?

5. Why did you choose this article?

6. Write five adjectives in the article.

   a
   b
   c
   d
   e

7. Does the title match the article's content? How?

8. How often do you use public transportation? When?

9. Do you think people should use public transportation more? Why?

10. What two adjectives would you use to describe the public transportation where you live? Why?

    a
    b

> "A railroad station? That was sort of a primitive airport,
> only you didn't have to take a cab 20 miles out of town to reach it."
> –Russell Baker (1925-2019), American journalist

Researching Natural Disasters

Student Name: _____ Date: _____

What sort of natural disasters happen in your country? What kind of natural disasters are there in our world? Find a video on a famous natural disaster. Watch the video and take some notes. Then select at least two (2) images related to the event you chose, and answer the questions below.

1 Which natural disaster did you choose? Why?

2 Describe the event. Where and when did it happen?

3 What were the natural conditions that contributed to this event?

4 What were some of the consequences of this natural disaster?

5 Describe the two (2) pictures you selected.

    a

    b

6 What caught your attention about these images?

7 How has the local community been changed by this natural disaster? Has the area recovered?

8 Is there a way to predict this type of natural disaster?

9 Write five idioms or expressions related to natural disasters.

    a

    b

    c

    d

    e

10 Moving forward, what can people do to better prepare for future disasters?

> "This is the moment when we must come together to save this planet. Let us resolve that we will not leave our children a world where the oceans rise and famine spreads and terrible storms devastate our lands."
> –Barack Obama (1961-), American politician and former President of the United States

Preparing for Natural Disasters

Student Name: _____ Date: _____

While many disasters occur with little to no warning, being aware of natural risks in your community and planning ahead for these emergencies can save lives. Choose one natural disaster and find an article with information on how to prepare and survive this emergency situation. Then, answer the following questions.

1 Describe the natural disaster you chose. What kind of damage can it cause?

2 What are two (2) things the article recommends doing to prepare ahead of the disaster?

    a

    b

3 What are two (2) things the article recommends doing during the disaster to stay safe?

    a

    b

4 Write five vocabulary words related to natural disasters.

    a

    b

    c

    d

    e

5 Which natural disaster(s) are you most at risk for where you live?

6 In the case of a mandatory evacuation, where would you go?

7 What personal items would you take with you during an evacuation? Why?

8 What would you leave behind in an evacuation? Why?

9 What, in your opinion, was the most helpful piece of advice in this article/video?

10 Which type of natural disaster are you the most anxious about? Why?

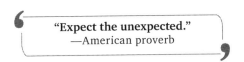
"Expect the unexpected."
—American proverb

Going Green

Student Name: _____ Date: _____

Do you know what it means to "go green?" Test your knowledge on common eco-friendly practices with **National Geographic's "Green Lifestyle Quiz"** (link below). Then, find a partner and ask them the following questions.

1 Did you enjoy the quiz? How many questions did you get right (out of 10 total)?

2 Which answers surprised you?

3 How else can we help the environment? Name one tip you knew before watching the video.

4 Do you consider yourself an environmentalist? Why or why not?

5 What is one thing you already do to help make your city cleaner and greener?

6 What is one thing you would like to do to help make your neighborhood cleaner and greener?

7 What are five ideas on how to live "greener"?

    a

    b

    c

    d

    e

8 There is a popular expression, "Think globally, act locally." What do you think it means?

9 What reforms would you like to see to help protect the environment?

10 What are some environmental success since you were born?

> "When one tugs at a single thing in nature,
> he finds it attached to the rest of the world."
> —John Muir (1838-1914), American naturalist and author

Talking About Taxes

Student Name: _____ Date: _____

Most governments use different kinds of taxes to fund a variety of government programs (education, defense, and social services). Citizens across the world have different ideas about how their governments should tax them. Who should pay taxes? What activities should be taxed, and how high should the tax be? Which taxes should be increased or decreased? Why?

What do you think? Find an article on the Internet (in English) about a tax reform that you would like to share with your classmates. Read the article, summarize it, and be prepared to discuss.

Title: _____
Web address: _____
Author: _____ Length: _____
Publication: _____ Publication date: _____

1. What's the main idea? Please summarize the tax reform in your own words.

2. What kinds of sources were quoted? How many?

3. What are the problems regarding the tax system discussed?

4. Is the article in favor of, or against, the tax reform discussed? Why?

5. What are the strongest arguments presented? Why?

6. What are the weakest arguments presented? Why?

7. What do you think about the proposed tax reform? Why?

8. Do you believe that the tax problems discussed are serious problems? Why or why not?

9. What are some other ideas that you have heard to improve the tax system in the United States?

10. What two adjectives would you use to describe the current tax system? Why?
    a.
    b.

> "In this world nothing can be said to be certain, except death and taxes."
> —Benjamin Franklin (1706-1790), American statesman and scientist

Extension Activities

1. APPRECIATING YOUR STYLE! (PG. 40)

What's new in the world of fashion? Create a collage or poster board presentation of the clothing or fashion trend you read about using pictures from magazines, catalogs, and the Internet. Share a picture of your work on the class blog and explain your collage in small groups.

2. EXPLORING AMERICAN SOCIAL ETIQUETTE (PG. 41)

What does politeness mean to you? Do you have a pet peeve about other people's behavior? Create a short video sharing your feelings and beliefs.

3. HANDLING CULTURE SHOCK (PG. 42)

What is culture shock? Write a short essay explaining culture shock and providing advice to recent arrivals in the United States. Share your video on the class blog and assist immigrants and international students in managing culture shock!

4. REDUCING STRESS AND INCREASING HAPPINESS (PG. 43)

How can people live happier, healthier lives? Create a three to four-minute video providing your best tips for living a happier, healthier life and how to apply them. Upload your video to the class blog and help others lead reduce their stress and increase their happiness!

5. EXAMINING A TED TALK (PG. 44)

Can you summarize and evaluate the TED talk that you watched for your classmates? Record a 60 to 90-second video of yourself giving a review of the TED Talk you selected. Why did you choose it? What was the main idea? How persuasive was the TED talk? Why?

6. TAKING PUBLIC TRANSPORTATION (PG. 45)

What should people know about public transportation in your area? Give a three to four-minute presentation providing information on how to use – or improve – public transportation.

7. RESEARCHING NATURAL DISASTERS (PG. 46)

a. Share your research on a specific natural disaster with your classmates in a short presentation with 8-10 slides.

b. Write an executive summary for the natural disaster you researched and discuss the natural conditions and consequences of this event. Share your executive summary on the class blog.

8. PREPARING FOR NATURAL DISASTERS (PG. 47)

How can people better prepare for natural disasters? Write a 300 to 500 word short essay about how people can do to better prepare for natural disasters. Cite sources, give examples, and help your classmates.

9. GOING GREEN (PG. 48)

What can your city do to become environmentally cleaner and healthier? Write a 300-500 word op-ed article for a local newspaper. Provide specific, realistic steps that your city could take to achieve this goal. Upload your op-ed to the class blog and assist your city in becoming greener!

10. TALKING ABOUT TAXES (PG. 49)

How could the American tax system be better? Write a letter containing your views and ideas on improving the tax system. You may want to send it to your local elected officials. Make your voice heard and contribute to healthy discussions on public policy!

Exploring New Career Opportunities

TOPICS:

Collecting Advice on Writing Professional Emails

Student Name: _____ Date: _____

Please find a short article that helps professionals successfully write emails – in English. You might search the Harvard Business Review, The Economist, the New York Times, and other appropriate sources. Read the article, take notes, summarize, and review it for your classmates.

Title: _____

Web address: _____

Author: _____ Length: _____

Publication: _____ Publication date: _____

1. Please describe the article. What's the main idea?

2. What writing tips did the article provide?

3. How practical did you find the advice? Why?

4. What was the strongest part? Why?

5. How could the article have been improved?

6. Who do think is the target audience for this article? Why?

7. Why did you choose this particular article?

8. Based on what you've learned, what makes an effective email? Why?

9. How many articles (a, an, the) appeared in the article? Circle and count them. Write an original sentence with each below.

   a: _____

   an: _____

   the: _____

10. How would you rate the article on a scale of 1–5, with 5 being the highest? Why?

> "I do love email. Wherever possible I try to communicate asynchronously. I'm really good at email."
> —Elon Musk (1971-), American entrepreneur and TESLA founder

Mastering Email Etiquette

Student Name: _____ Date: _____

We have all been misunderstood at some time or other. Email, while an essential professional tool, can also cause misunderstandings in school and at work.

How can we prevent future misunderstandings? Answer the following questions about email etiquette and discuss with your classmates.

1 What are five ways that emails can be misunderstood?

     a

     b

     c

     d

     e

2 Have your emails ever been misunderstood? Why? What happened? Briefly share a misadventure in email writing using the space below. Please include the following details:

- Who was the audience?
- What were the text, context, and subtext of the email?
- What was the source of the misunderstanding?
- How could the misunderstanding have been avoided?

_____

_____

_____

_____

_____

_____

_____

_____

> "Whatever you can say in a meeting, you can put in an email. If I have questions, I'll tell you via email."
> —Mark Cuban (1958-), American entrepreneur and basketball team owner

Search & Share

Reproducible

Collecting Resume Advice on the Internet

Student Name: _____ Date: _____

Please find a short article (500-1500 words) in English that helps job seekers successfully write better resumes that you would like to share with your classmates. You might search the Online Writing Lab, Harvard Business Review, The Economist, The Muse, and other appropriate sources. Read the article, take notes, summarize, and review it for your classmates.

Title: _____

Web address: _____

Author: _____   Length: _____

Publication: _____   Publication date: _____

1   Please describe the article. What's the main idea?

2   What writing tips did the article provide?

4   What was the strongest part? Why?

5   How practical did you find the advice? Why?

6   What do you think the five most interesting or phrases were? Can you list them?

    a

    b

    c

    d

    e

7   Who do you think is the target audience for this article? Why?

8   Why did you choose this article?

9   What is one thing you learned from this article that you didn't know before?

10 How would you rate the article on a scale of 1–5, with 5 being the highest? Why?

> "Big jobs usually go to the men who prove their ability to outgrow small ones."
> —Theodore Roosevelt (1858-1919), 26th President of the United States

Collecting Advice on Writing Effective Cover Letters

Student Name: _____ Date: _____

How do we write compelling cover letters? Please find a short article that helps professionals successfully write cover letters – in English. Read the article, take notes, summarize, and review it for your classmates.

Title: _____

Author: _____ Length: _____

Publication: _____ Publication date: _____

1 What's the main idea?

2 What cover letter writing tips did the article provide?

3 What are some possible mistakes that job applicants can make on cover letters?

4 What was the article's strongest part? Why?

5 How would you improve the article?

6 Why did you choose this specific article on writing cover letters?

7 Based on what you've learned, what makes an effective cover letter? Why?

8 Why do you think some people dislike writing cover letters? What mistakes can a writer make?

9 Why are cover letters important for applicants? For employers?

10 How important do you think first impressions are in professional situations? Why?

> **Letters are something from you.**
> **It's a different kind of intention than writing an e-mail.**
> —Keanu Reeves (1964-), American actor

Sharing Best Practices for Job Interviews

Student Name: _____ Date: _____

Can you offer some advice on how to answer questions on a job interview? What are some best practices for job interviews? What should applicants in your field expect on a job interivew? Please find a short video (5-10 minutes) that helps college students and young professionals learn how to conduct effective job interviews – in English - to share with your classmates. Watch the video, take notes, summarize, and review it.

Video title: _____

Web address: _____

Length: _____ Creator: _____

1. Please describe the video. What's the main idea?

2. What interview tips did the video provide?

3. What was the best part? Why?

4. How could the video have been improved? Why?

5. Why did you choose this video?

6. What is one thing you learned from this video that you didn't know before?

7. How would you rate the video on a scale of 1–5, with 5 being the highest? Why?

8. What are five common interview questions? Can you list them?

   a.
   b.
   c.
   d.
   e.

9. What are three questions you want to be asked on a job interview?

10. What are 5 positive adejctives that describe you?

> "Hiring is a manager's most important job."
> —Peter F. Drucker (1909-2005), American management consultant and author

Sharing Best Practices for Skype Job Interviews

Student Name: _____ Date: _____

Can you offer some advice on how to interview over Skype? What are some best practices for conducting a successful interview online? Please find a short video (5-10 minutes) that helps college students and young professionals learn how to conduct effective job interviews – in English – via video chat. Watch the video, take notes, summarize, and review it.

Video title: _____

Web address: _____

Length: _____ Creator: _____

1. Please describe the video. What's the main idea?

2. What tips for interviewing over Skype did the video provide?

3. What was the strongest part? Why?

4. How practical did you find the advice? Why?

5. Why did you choose this video?

6. What is one thing you learned from this video that you didn't know before?

7. How would you rate the video on a scale of 1–5, with 5 being the highest? Why?

8. Based on your resume, what are five questions the employer might ask you?

   a.
   b.
   c.
   d.
   e.

9. Would you prefer to be interviewed on the telephone or Skype? Why?

10. What are five adjectives that describe the ideal candidate?

> "Passion plus competency, not just competency alone, is key to securing employment."
> —Richard Bolles (1927-2017), American author of *What Color is Your Parachute?*

Conducting Effective Informational Interviews

Student Name: _____ Date: _____

What are informational interviews? How can we use them to explore and further our careers? Please find a short article (500-1500 words) that helps college students and young professionals learn how to conduct effective informational interviews – in English - to share with your classmates. You might search The Muse, the New York Times, Forbes, and other appropriate sources. Summarize the article, and review it for your classmates.

Title: _____

Author: _____ Length: _____

Publication: _____ Publication date: _____

1 Please describe the article. What's the main idea?

2 What informational interview tips did the article provide?

3 How practical did you find the advice? Why?

4 What was the strongest part? Why?

5 Why did you choose this article?

6 What is one thing you learned from this article that you didn't know before?

7 How would you rate the article on a scale of 1–5, with 5 being the highest? Why?

8 Why do you think informational interviews are so popular?

9 What five questions would you like to ask in an informational interview?

    a

    b

    c

    d

    e

10 Who would you like to conduct an informational interview with? Why?

> "In today's world, he or she who gets hired is not necessarily the one who can do that job best; but, the one who knows the most about how to get hired."
> —Richard Bolles (1927-2017), American author of *What Color is Your Parachute?*

Exploring Engineering in Daily Life

Student Name: _____ Date: _____

Are you interested in science, technology, and engineering? Find an illuminating article documenting how science and technology influence our daily life from **wired.com** or **popsci.com** (**Popular Science**) and fill in this worksheet. Be prepared to share your summary and evaluation with your classmates in small group discussions.

Title: _____

Web address: _____

Author: _____ Date: _____

1 What's the main idea of the article you chose?

2 How many sources does the author cite? What is the most recent source?

3 What kind of illustrations were used?

4 What is the strongest features of the article?

5 Write five new vocabulary words, idioms, or expressions related to the topic.

  a

  b

  c

  d

  e

6 What did you learn from the article that you did not know before?

7 Why did you choose this article?

8 How would you rate the article on a scale of 1–5, with 5 being the highest? Why?

9 Why is engineering an important field today?

10 What technological changes have you seen in your lifetime?

> "Any sufficiently advanced technology is indistinguishable from magic."
> —Arthur C. Clarke (1917-2008), English writer

Learning More About a Famous Person You Admire

Student Name: _____ Date: _____

Which famous person do you respect and look up to? How did they create their lives? Outstanding individuals often believe they have made crucial decisions that led to their future success. Find a video about someone you admire. Who is this person? What did they do? Learn more about a personal hero by watching a documentary or news feature. Be ready to discuss the video about your hero with your classmates.

1 Who did you choose as a personal hero?

2 What video or documentary did you find?

3 Can you describe the person's background or childhood?

4 What did you learn about this person that you didn't know before?

5 What obstacles did this person overcome?

6 What were some achievements or highlights of their life?

7 What was the most interesting part of the biography for you? Why?

8 How would you rate the video on a scale of 1–5, with 5 being the highest? Why?

9 What else would you like to know about this person? Why?

10 Why is this individual a personal hero?

> **"Be yourself. Everyone else is already taken."**
> —Oscar Wilde (1856–1900), Irish playwright

Exploring New Career Opportunities

Student Name: _____ Date: _____

Choosing a career path can be a difficult decision. However, researching occupations that best fit your abilities and interests is a good place to start! Explore a career at **glassdoor.com**, which provides helpful information on duties, education, compensation, and predictions for hundreds of occupations. You can also consult the Occupational Outlook Handbook (OOH), and online tool from The U.S. Department of Labor, for additional information.

Choose a job listing from the site that interests you, and answer the following questions.

Job Title: _____
Company: _____
Experience Level: _____ Date Posted: _____

1 What duties and responsibilities are listed in the job description?

2 What training and skills does this job require?

3 What are the working conditions like?

4 Are there opportunities for job growth in this position?

5 Is this position currently in high demand? Why or why not?

6 What benefits (health insurance, paid time off, etc.) are included with this position?

7 What are the national average earnings for this position? City average?

8 What are the disadvantages of holding this job? Why?

9 What else would you like to know about this job?

10 Why did you choose this position? Why might this career match your skills and personality?

> "Do the best you can until you know better.
> Then when you know better, do better."
> —Maya Angelou (1928–2014), American poet

1. COLLECTING ADVICE ON WRITING PROFESSIONAL EMAILS (PG. 53)

Are you confident in writing professional emails? Compose and send an email to your teacher asking about your performance in the class so far and how you can further improve.

2. MASTERING EMAIL ETIQUETTE (PG. 54)

How can people avoid being misunderstood when writing emails? Write an email on how people can avoid being misunderstood in emails. Share your work on the class blog – and your teacher.

3. COLLECTING RESUME ADVICE ON THE INTERNET (PG. 55)

What does a successful job seeker's resume look like? Create a resume or revise your current one by applying the advice you read. Send your resume to your teacher for feedback.

4. COLLECTING ADVICE ON WRITING EFFECTIVE COVER LETTERS (PG. 56)

What does an effective cover letter look like? Write a 3-4 paragraph cover letter as if you were applying for a job listing you have seen in person or online. Send your cover letter to your teacher for feedback with a link to the job listing.

5. SHARING BEST PRACTICES FOR JOB INTERVIEWS (PG. 57)

Are you ready for a job interview for a specific position? Conduct a mock job interview for a position that you want. Then, switch roles.

6. SHARING BEST PRACTICES FOR SKYPE JOB INTERVIEWS (PG. 58)

Are you ready for an interview via Skype? Conduct a mock job interview for a position that you want. Then, switch roles.

7. CONDUCTING EFFECTIVE INFORMATIONAL INTERVIEWS (PG. 59)

Who do you want to talk to about their career path? Find an individual to conduct an informational interview with. Write 20 questions you would like to ask them about their specific career. Send your questions to your teacher for feedback. Include background information on the professional.

8. EXPLORING ENGINEERING IN DAILY LIFE (PG. 60)

What product or improvement in a current product would you like to see in the future? Write a 300 to 500 word memo to investors describing a future product or improvement in an already-existing product. Pitch your product and persuade the reader to invest in your idea.

9. LEARNING MORE ABOUT A FAMOUS PERSON YOU ADMIRE (PG. 61)

What are/were the significant events of your hero's life? Create a timeline of your hero's life and share your work on the class blog.

10. EXPLORING NEW CAREER OPPORTUNITIES (PG. 62)

Are you ready to be hired for the position you are interested in? Write a cover letter and resume for that position. Prepare five questions you would like to be asked if you were to be interviewed for the job. Then, prepare another three questions you would ask the potential employer. Send your cover letter, resume, and eight questions with a link to this position's information to your English teacher for feedback.

F Enjoying and Keeping Money

TOPICS:

Building a Better Budget

Student Name: _____ Date: _____

Where would you like to live in the United States? What would it cost to live your American dream in California, the "Golden State"? The cost of living often depends on location, so you need to consider many things when creating a realistic budget.

The California Career Resource Network has created an interactive website called **CACareerZone.org** with a tool to help estimate budgets. Check it out.

1   Were you able to successfully complete the budget process? If not, why not?

2   Did you find any surprises? What?

3   Where does most of your money go?

4   Where would you like to spend more? Why?

5   Where would you like to spend less? Why?

6   What do you think are some advantages to living in California? Why?

7   What's your first choice for a possible home in California? Why?

8   What's your second choice for a possible home in California? Why?

9   Can you compare the two locations? How are the costs similar? Different?

10   How do you save money? Can you share a few suggestions?

> "A penny saved is a penny earned."
> —Benjamin Franklin (1706-1790), American author and statesman

Reviewing Movies

Student Name: _____ Date: _____

Can you recommend an excellent movie? First, select one of your favorite films. Second, go to **imdb.com** or **metacritic.com** and research your selected film. Third, take notes. A strong movie review will combine both facts and opinions. Use this short worksheet to describe the movie and prepare to share your informed opinion with your classmates.

Movie Title: _____ Length: _____

Year released: _____ Director: _____

Actors/Actresses: _____ Awards: _____

How many times have you watched the movie? Where?

Plot Information:

1 Where and when does the movie take place?

2 Who is the main character? Can you briefly describe another important character?

3 What happens in the movie?

4 What is the best part? Why?

5 Does the movie surprise the audience? How?

6 Who do you think would like this movie?

7 How could the movie be better?

8 How would you rate the movie on a scale of 1–5, with 5 being the highest? Why?

9 Can you choose five adjectives to describe this movie? Why?

> "Every great film should seem new every time you see it."
> —Roger Ebert (1942–2013), American film critic

Choosing a Local Restaurant

Student Name: _____ Date: _____

Do you use Yelp.com yet? Find and share a positive review for a local restaurant that you like. Pick a favorite local restaurant, do some research, and pick the best review— in English. Use this worksheet to tell us about the review.

Remember restaurant reviews should provide examples and details. Tell us about a special restaurant—in English—and help us find a place to eat delicious food.

Restaurant: _____ Location: _____

Reviewer: _____ Review: _____

1   Why did you pick this review?

2   How does the reviewer describe the restaurant? What kind of food does it serve?

3   When was the review written?

4   What do you know about the reviewer?

5   What does the reviewer say about the restaurant's atmosphere?

6   How did the reviewer describe the restaurant's service?

7   What did the reviewer eat?

8   What was the best part of the restaurant review?

9   Does the reviewer recommend the restaurant? Why?

10 How often have you been to the restaurant? Why do you recommend this restaurant?

> "One man's meat is another man's poison."
> —Latin proverb

Eating in L.A.

Student Name: _____ Date: _____

What comes to your mind when you think of Los Angeles (L.A.)? What have you heard about L.A.? The City of Angels is the largest city in California and the second-most populous in the United States. Its famous amusement parks, marvelous museums, and fashion boutiques attract tourists from all over the world. L.A. also boasts an astonishing range of cafes and restaurants. Choose one restaurant or cafe in Los Angeles and plan a special meal.

Name: _____

Location: _____

1 What kind of food do you enjoy most?

2 Why did you choose this restaurant for your special meal?

3 Does the place have good ratings online? What positive review comments attracted your attention?

4 How did you first hear about this place?

5 Write five new vocabulary words, idioms, or expressions related to restaurants.

    a

    b

    c

    d

    e

6 What's your favorite aspect of the establishment's look and ambience?

7 What makes this place different from other restaurants you've eaten at?

8 How much do you expect to spend on this wonderful meal?

9 What dish on the menu are you most excited to try?

10 Who would you like to share this memorable meal in L.A. with? Why?

> **"I have eaten very well in Los Angeles. Marvelously!"**
> —Gustavo Dudamel (1981-) Venezuelan violinist and conductor of the LA Philharmonic

Buying a Car

Student Name: _____ Date: _____

What car would you like to own? What cars are you curious about? Gather as much information about the model car as you can. Then answer the following questions.

Manufacturer: _____

Model: _____

Year: _____ Cost: _____

1 Which car did you choose to research? Why?

2 What are your top two (2) priorities when it comes to choosing a new car?

    a

    b

3 What is your budget like for buying a car? How did you decide on this budget?

4 What are the advantages (benefits) of having a car?

5 What are some disadvantages (costs) of having a car?

6 Describe the model, year, mileage, color, and features of the car you want.

7 What is your favorite feature of this car?

8 What is your least favorite feature of this car? Why?

9 Write five useful vocabulary words, idioms, or expressions related to the topic.

    a

    b

    c

    d

    e

10 Who do you think is the ideal consumer for this car? Why?

> **"Cars are the sculptures of our everyday lives."**
> –Chris Bangle (1956-), American automotive designer

Should You Buy It?

Student Name: _____ Date: _____

Product reviews are increasingly popular, and you can find many places to share reviews. For your next class, pick a consumer product to review. Do some research online about the product. Find at least two sources of information. Then fill in this worksheet and create a product review. Share with your classmates.

Product: _____ Company: _____

Source: _____ Date: _____

1 Do you own the product?

2 What is the purpose of the product?

3 Who is the target audience for this product? Who usually uses it?

4 How is the product used?

5 What is the best feature of this consumer product?

6 What competitors does the product have? Does this product have a competitive advantage?

7 Are there some possible dangers or misuses of the product?

8 What did you learn from your research about this product?

9 Would you recommend this product to your classmates? Do you have some concerns about this product?

10 How would you rate the product on a scale of 1–5, with five being the highest? Why?

> "The customer is always right."
> —American proverb

Giving to Charities and Good Causes

Student Name: _____ Date: _____

How can you help make the world a better place? Do you give money to good causes or charities? Do you volunteer your time with an organization that helps people, animals, or society?

The word "charity" comes from a Latin term meaning "kindness toward others less fortunate than ourselves." Groups or non-profit organizations that help those who are struggling by giving them goods, money, and services are called "charities." Search online for information about a charity or non-profit organization that helps people. Then, answer the following questions and share your responses with your classmates.

1. What is the name of the charity or non-profit? Why did you choose this organization?

2. What type of organization are they? What does the organization do?

3. What are the organization's core beliefs, values, philosophy, or world view?

4. How successful has the organization been so far? In what ways?

5. Has the organization been involved in any controversies or scandals? Give an example.

6. What is the non-profit's current slogan and/or main campaign?

7. Who supports this charity or non-profit organization?

8. What are three reasons that people support this specific charity or non-profit?

   a
   b
   c

9. Why do you think so many Americans support charities and non-profits?

10. Do you think it is better to give your money or time to help others? Why?

> "The charity that is a trifle to us can be precious to others."
> –Homer (751-651 BCE), ancient Greek poet and author

Writing an App Review

Student Name: _____ Date: _____

Please research an application available on the App Store or Google Play. You may want to limit your search to free apps. Find out as much as you can about this app through personal use and/or online research. Then, review the app and share with your classmates.

1. Describe the app you chose. Is it a game or a productivity tool? Something else?

2. Why did you choose this app?

3. Who is the target audience for this app?

4. Are there any similar apps available? What are they?

5. What is your favorite thing about this app? Why?

6. Are there any user reviews or ratings (in English) for this app? What is the overall or average rating?

7. What did you learn about this app that you didn't know before?

8. Do you recommend the app to your classmates? Why or why not?

9. How would you rate the app on a scale of 1–5, with five being the highest? Why?

10. How would your life be different without smartphones and apps? Why?

> "Technology is a useful servant but a dangerous master."
> —Christian Lous Lange (1869-1938), Norwegian politician and Nobel Prize recipient

 **Search & Share**

Responding to Yelp! Reviews

Student Name: _____ Date: _____

Bad reviews aren't all bad; sometimes they provide valuable feedback for businesses that want to improve. Find a negative review of a hotel, restaurant, or other business that describes a negative customer experience in detail. Then answer the following questions.

1 What is the name of the business?

2 What type of business is it? What services do they provide?

3 What complaints are made in the review? Are they related to service, efficiency, or something else?

4 What is the tone of the review? Does the reviewer come across as reasonable or rude? Why?

5 Is the criticism in the review constructive/helpful? Why or why not?

Now, imagine you are the owner or manager of this business. How would you respond to this customer's complaints and concerns? Write a brief response to the reviewer below.

_____

_____

_____

_____

_____

_____

_____

_____

> "The details are not the details. They make the design."
> —Charles Eames (1907-1978), American designer

1. BUILDING A BETTER BUDGET (PG. 66)

How do you think your life will be financially different in the future? Create a possible budget for two years into the future and post it to the class blog. Feel free to share your assumtions

2. REVIEWING MOVIES (PG. 67)

Are there any movies that you would like to recommend? Write a 200 to 500-word movie review and include at least one illustration and cite the source. Share your review on the class blog.

3. CHOOSING A LOCAL RESTAURANT (PG. 68)

What restaurants would you like for others to enjoy or avoid? Write a short 100-250 word Yelp review for a restaurant of your choice. Be as specific as possible and include a photograph.

4. EATING IN L.A. (PG. 69)

Describe a special meal in Los Angeles. Help us see the food and imagine the meal with vivid details of the experience. Share your descriptive essay on the class blog.

5. BUYING A CAR (PG. 70)

What would the people you love and respect think of your choice of a car? Write an email to a friend or relative explaining your choice of a new car.

Do you have a dream car? Compare your dream car with the car you selected in a venn diagram. Consider comfort, entertainment and safety features.

6. SHOULD YOU BUY IT? (PG. 71)

Can you write a persuasive product review? Write an Amazon product review of 100 to 250 words. You may include properly cited illustrations.

Did the product you reviewed exist a decade ago? How did it change? Compare an older model with the most current version in a venn diagram.

7. GIVING TO CHARITIES AND GOOD CAUSES (PG. 72)

Write a short, persuasive email convincing your audience to contribute to a favorite charity or good cause.

Who should we give money to? Give a short, persuasive presentation convincing your classmates to contribute to a favorite charity or good cause.

8. WRITING AN APP REVIEW (PG. 73)

What makes an app good, effective, terrible, or defective? Write a 75 to 250 word review of an app you use on your phone's app store (e.g., the Apple Store, Google Play, etc.).

9. RESPONDING TO YELP! REVIEWS (PG. 74)

How would a concerned, savvy business-owner reply to critical Yelp reviews? Roleplay being a concerned, savvy business-owner and write a longer, more detailed response to your negative Yelp review. Consider the multiple audiences: the disatisfied customer; the many loyal customers; potential customers on Yelp; and your staff.

G   Travel

TOPICS:

Talking About My Hometown

Student Name: _____ Date: _____

All people are shaped by the place where they were born or grew up. Where were you born? Where did you grow up? What would you like to tell us about your hometown?

Please find a story on the Internet (in English) about your hometown or local region that you would like to share with your classmates. Read the article, print it out, and be prepared to discuss it.

Title: _____

Author: _____ Length: _____

Publication: _____ Publication date: _____

1 What's the main idea?

2 Were there any photos or illustrations? What kind?

3 What did you learn from this article?

4 What was the most interesting part for you?

5 How many sources were quoted?

6 What information was missing? What else should people know about your hometown?

7 Write five interesting vocabulary words, idioms, or expressions in the article. Provide definitions for new words.

　　a

　　b

　　c

　　d

　　e

8 How would you rate the article, on a scale of 1–5, with five being the highest? Why?

9 Why did you choose this article?

10 How has your hometown changed in the last decade?

> "The city must never be confused with the words that describe it.
> And yet, between one and the other, there is a connection."
> —Italo Calvino (1923-1985), Italian novelist

Being at the Beach

Student Name: _____ Date: _____

Do you like going to the beach? Beautiful beaches attract tourists from around the world and can remain in people's memories forever. Which is your favorite beach so far? Search for a video about your favorite beach or one you would like to visit.

Title: _____
Author: _____
Length: _____ Date: _____

1. Describe the beach you chose. Where is it located?

2. According to the video, what makes this beach special?

3. Is the beach considered a popular tourist spot or a hidden gem? Why?

4. What other attractions are near this beach? Which ones interest you most?

5. What did you learn about this beach that you did not know before?

6. What did you like about the video you chose?

7. How would you improve the video?

8. How would you rate the video on a scale of 1–5, with 5 being the highest? Why?

9. Find three proverbs or sayings related to beaches.

   a.

   b.

   c.

10. Why did you choose this beach? What does your ideal beach day look like?

> "The sea, once it casts its spell, holds one in its net of wonder forever."
> —Jacques Yves Cousteau (1910-1997), French explorer

Sightseeing Through Social Media

Student Name: _____ Date: _____

Social media isn't just limited to individual and company accounts. Sometimes even cities have social media! Let's explore a new city together. Find an active social media account that belongs to a city or the city's tourism office/bureau and monitor it for a week. What did you learn?

City: _____

Account Name: _____ Social Network: _____

1   What city does this social media account represent? Why did you choose this city?

2   What kind of content does this account post?

3   Who runs the account?

4   Can you find an example of a hidden gem that is featured on this account?

5   Can you find an example of a tourist trap that is featured on this account?

6   Is there a place or event in the city that you would visit or attend based on what you have seen on this account? What is it?

7   Do you think this account represents the city well? Why or why not?

8   What would you improve on or do differently if you ran this account?

9   How would you rate the account's content on a scale of 1–5, with 5 being the highest? Why?

10   What did you learn about this city through the account that you didn't know before?

> **"What is the city but the people?"**
> —William Shakespeare (1564-1616), English playwright

TripAdvisor: Exploring a New City

Student Name: _____ Date: _____

Let's explore a foreign city together! Go to **tripadvisor.com** and type in "Things to Do" in the city that you wish to visit. Spend some time looking at the pictures and read the descriptions of the many places you can visit in that city. Share this information with your classmates.

1   What city did you visit?

2   What are two facts about this city?

3   Were there any illustrations? What kind?

4   What did you learn about this city?

5   What else would you like to know about this city?

6   What was the most interesting part for you? Why?

7   Identify five special places in this city.

   a

   b

   c

   d

   e

8   How would you rate the TripAdvisor site on a scale of 1–5, with 5 being the highest? Why?

9   Are you hoping to go to this city? How long would you stay for?

10   Why are you interested in this city?

> "The bold adventurer succeeds the best."
> —Ovid (43 B.C.E.–17 C.E.) Roman poet

Looking at Languages

Student Name: _____ Date: _____

All of the world's languages, estimated at least 6,000, have stories. English, for example, has become the world's most influential language in business and science over the last 50 years.

Besides English, what language are you curious about? Can you tell us more about another language? Go to to Wikipedia to gain more information about another language spoken on planet Earth. Take notes and answer the following questions. Discuss your research with your classmates.

1. What language did you choose to study today? Why did you pick it?

2. Where is this language usually spoken? How many people, approximately, speak it?

3. Can you tell me a bit more about this language?

4. Where is this language an official language?

5. Is this an ancient or modern language? How do you know?

6. What are five words that English borrows from this language?

   a.
   b.
   c.
   d.
   e.

7. Who are some famous people who speak this language?

8. What music or movies are created in this language? Can you give some examples?

9. How similar is this language to English? In what ways?

10. In what situations would knowing how to speak this language be helpful?

> "The more you praise and celebrate your life, the more there is in life to celebrate."
> —Oprah Winfrey (1954–), American star and philanthropist

Touring California

Student Name: _____ Date: _____

Have you been to or lived in California? What images come to your mind when you think of California? California often attracts visitors for plenty of reasons, including its weather, natural beauty, tourist sites, and life style. Find an article that shares tourist tips and information about California.

Title: _____
Author: _____ Length: _____
Publication: _____ Publication date: _____

1 Describe the article you chose. What is the main idea?

2 How is the article organized?

3 Which locations does the article mention?

4 What did you learn about California?

5 Write three slang terms used in the article – or in California.

 a

 b

 c

 Write an additional two new/interesting words from the article.

 d

 e

6 Why did you choose this article?

7 What else would you like to know about this topic?

8 How would you rate the article on a scale of 1–5, with 5 being the highest? Why?

9 After reading the article, which California tourist site are you most interested in visiting?

10 What would you like to do on a week-long vacation in California? Why?

> **"California is America – only more so."**
> —Wallace E. Stegner (1909-1993) American historian

Visiting Brazil

Student Name: _____ Date: _____

Brazil awaits you! Where would you like to go? What would you like to see? Share your answers with a partner!

1. What do you already know about Brazil?

2. How will you prepare for your trip to Brazil?

3. Are you taking anyone with you on your vacation? Why or why not?

4. Which attractions will you see? Why?

5. What is your travel budget? How will you choose to spend it?

6. What kinds of Brazilian food are you interested in tasting?

7. What are five photographs you would like to take in Brazil?

   a.

   b.

   c.

   d.

   e.

8. What Brazilian movies, songs or musicians are you familiar with?

9. Why do you think so many global tourists visit Brazil every year?

10. What are five adjectives that describe the landscape/geography of Brazil?

> "They have a joy for life in Brazil unlike any country I've ever seen."
> —Morena Baccarin (1979-), Brazilian-American actress

Visiting France

Student Name: _____ Date: _____

Have you been to France yet? What would you like to see and do in France? Imagine you have free airfare to France and plan a week-long trip there. Share your travel plans with your classmates!

1   Where will you go?

2   How can you prepare for your trip to France? What would you like to know?

3   Who are you taking with you? Why?

4   What photographs do you want to take? Why?

5   How will you get around France? Why?

6   What will you do? How will you spend your days?

7   What French food are you interested in tasting? Why?

8   Write five English vocabulary words, idioms, or expressions that come from the local language.

     a

     b

     c

     d

     e

9   What French movies have you seen? What are some movies set in France?

10   What are you looking forward to doing in France? Why?

> "**Paris is always a good idea.**"
> —Audrey Hepburn (1929-1993), English actress

Visiting Japan

Student Name: ———————————————— Date: ————————————

You're a winner! You've been chosen to spend a week anywhere in Japan. Pick a location in Japan that you would like to visit and plan your trip. Share with your classmates!

1 What do you already know about Japan?

2 Where are you visiting? Why did you choose this place?

3 What are you planning to take with you to this place? Who is going with you?

4 How will you prepare for this visit? What movies would you like to watch?

5 What do you want to see and photograph? Why?

6 Which attractions in Tokyo are you visiting? Why?

7 What kinds of Japanese food do you like? What would you like to try?

8 Write five English words that come from Japan. (Example: ninja)

    a

    b

    c

    d

    e

9 Why do you think Japan is so popular as a tourist destination?

10 What are five adjectives that can describe Japanese culture?

> "Every one of a hundred thousand cities around the world had its own special sunset and it was worth going there, just once, if only to see the sun go down."
> —Ryu Murakami (1952–), Japanese novelist and director

Visiting Vietnam

Student Name: _____ Date: _____

Vietnam attracts tourists from across the planet. Imagine you won a free, one week vacation to Vietnam. What would you like to see and do in Vietnam? Read an article about visiting Vietnam to prepare for your trip.

1   What are a few things you know about Vietnam?

2   Would you prefer to visit a city, the countryside, or both? Why?

3   Who would you like to travel to Vietnam with? Why?

4   How would you prepare for a week-long trip to Vietnam?

5   What are five special places/tourist destinations in Vietnam?

     a

     b

     c

     d

     e

6   What advice did you find about visiting Vietnam?

7   Where will you start? Why?

8   Do you like Vietnamese food? Would you like to try some new dishes? Which ones?

9   What do you most want to see in Vietnam? Why?

10   Why do you think Vietnam has become such a popular travel destination?

> "If you haven't visited Ha Long Bay, you haven't been to Vietnam."
> —Popular tourist slogan

1. TALKING ABOUT MY HOMETOWN (PG. 78)

How well did the article represent your hometown or local region? Write a 400-500 word reacion summarizing and responding to the article. What else would you like us to know about your hometown?

2. BEING AT THE BEACH (PG. 79)

What should visitors to this beach know? Write a tourist brochure for the beach.

3. SIGHTSEEING THROUGH SOCIAL MEDIA (PG. 80)

Where in the world would you like to visit? Why? Write a short memo the city's social media manager giving your observations and feedback.

4. TRIPADVISOR: EXPLORING A NEW CITY (PG. 81)

If you had to recommend a place for others to visit, what would it be? Pick one city outside the United States that you recommend. Write a short, persuasive letter explaining your choice and share it on the class blog.

5. LOOKING AT LANGUAGES (PG. 82)

How similar is the language you chose to English? Compare and contrast English with this language with a chart. Be prepared to give a brief presentation to your classmates explaining your reasoning.

6. TOURING CALIFORNIA (PG. 83)

What's your idea of a perfect California day? Create a one-day schedule for a special day in a special place in California, the Golden State.

7. VISITING BRAZIL (PG. 84)

Write a letter inviting somebody to go on a one-week trip to Brazil. Share your vision!

8. VISITING FRANCE (PG. 85)

What do you know about France? Select and share 10 facts about France. (Example: Paris is the capital of France.)

9. VISITING JAPAN (PG. 86)

Where would you like to visit in Japan? Collect five to ten photographs of places in Japan that you would like to see. Explain your choices in small groups and express your preferences.

10. VISITING VIETNAM (PG. 87)

Where would you like to visit in Vietnam? Give a short presentation (two to five minutes) on a special place in Vietnam that you would like to visit. Include photos and cite your sources in your slides.

Enjoying Free Time

TOPICS:

How do you spend your time?

Student Name: _____ Date: _____

Enter the amount of time you spend on each of the following activities on a typical weekday. Use your best estimate or guess for each category.

Activity 1:

Activity	Hours	Minutes
attending classes		
attending religious services/praying		
commuting/driving		
doing chores		
eating and drinking		
playing sports and exercising		
sleeping		
socializing		
using your cell phone		
volunteering		
watching TV		
working		
other		

For any of the above activities, would you say that you spend more or less time on it compared to the amount of time you spent on it a year ago? Why?

Activity 2: Discuss your activities in small groups.

Bonus: Consider your own schedule for a week. Then compare your predicted schedule with your actual behaviors. How well do they match up?

> "All the treasures of the earth cannot bring back one lost moment."
> —French proverb

Sharing Muscial Tastes

Student Name: _____ Date: _____

Sharing musical tastes is a fun way to get to know others – a person's favorite band can say a lot about them! Do you have a favorite band or musician? Tell us about them! Use the following questions as prompts and do research as needed.

1. Describe your favorite band/musician. Who are they? What kind of music do they make?

2. Describe each person's role(s) in producing the music. Do they sing? Compose? Play instruments? Which ones?

3. Have you seen this artist/group in concert before? If not, would you like to?

4. Are they still making music? Why or why not?

5. What is your favorite piece of music by this artist/group? Why? What do you like about it?

6. Do you have a favorite music video by the artist(s)? Why is it your favorite?

7. Do you have a favorite album by the artist(s)? What is it?

8. What was your first impression of this artist/group? Has it changed?

9. Who would you recommend this artist/group to? Why?

10. What two questions would you ask the musician/band in an interview?

> "Music is life itself. What would this world be without good music?"
> —Louis Armstrong (1901-1971), American composer and Jazz musician

Sharing Restaurant Recommendations

Student Name: _____ Date: _____

Everyone has different opinions on which restaurants are the best of the best. We'd like to hear yours! Give us your recommendations on where to find the best breakfast food, pizza, and ethnic food of your choice (ex. Italian, Chinese, Mexican) locally. Then, answer the following questions and share your recommendations with the class!

Questions:	Best Breakfast:	Best Pizza:	Best Ethnic Food:
What is the name of the restaurant?			
How long has it been in business?			
Is this establishment part of a chain or independently owned?			
What is the average price of a meal at this establishment?			
What menu item is this place's "claim to fame?"			
What menu item do you order most frequently here? Do you have a "usual?"			
Why do you recommend this place? What makes it special?			
Name one advantage this eatery has over competitors.			
Name one disadvantage this eatery has over competitors.			
Does the average Yelp rating for this place fit your experience there? Why?			

"You learn a lot about someone when you share a meal together."
—Anthony Bourdain (1956-2018), American chef and author

TV or not TV (Is that a question?)

Student Name: _____ Date: _____

Search the Internet for a video (in English), taken from a current television show. You might want to try searching on **Hulu**, **Netflix**, or **nbc.com/video**

Choose a video segment (it's not necessary to watch more than ten minutes), watch it two times, and be prepared to discuss it with classmates.

TV series: _____ Type of show: _____

Title of episode: _____ Length: _____

Broadcast network: _____ Original airdate: _____

1 What's the show about?

2 Can you describe one or two of the main characters?

3 Where and when does the show take place? Is it set in our world or a fictional world?

4 Describe the scene you chose to watch. Was there a conversation? Conflict?

5 What do you think happens next? Why?

6 Did you enjoy the story? Why or why not?

7 What was the most interesting part for you? Why?

8 Write five noteworthy vocabulary words, idioms, or expressions from the TV show.

   a

   b

   c

   d

   e

9 How would you rate the video/TV show on a scale of 1–5, with five being the highest? Why?

10 Why did you choose this video to share with your classmates?

> "In the age of television, image becomes more important than substance."
> —S.I. Hayakawa (1906–1992), U.S. senator and linguist

 **Search & Share**

Enjoying a Great Game

Student Name: ——————————————— Date: ———————————————

Wow! What a great game! Think of a great sports match. Search for a video on the Internet (in English) about an exciting game, championship series, or rivalry. Collect information so you can tell your classmates about the exciting sports event. Here are two websites that might be worthwhile for you to visit: **espn.com** and **si.com** (Sports Illustrated). Use this worksheet to take notes.

Title: ———————————————————————————————
Web address: ————————————————————————————
Length: ———————————————————— Publication date: ——————————————

1 What sports event did you choose? Why?

2 What is the background to this great game? Can you describe the two rivals?

3 What happened in the game? Who won?

4 Which team did you want to win the match? Why?

5 Describe the final moments of the game. Were they suspenseful? Predictable?

6 Was there a star player in this particular game? Who was it?

7 What was your favorite part of the game? Why?

8 Write three sports vocabulary words, idioms, or expressions related to the game.

    a
    b
    c

9 How would you rate the game/match on a scale of 1–5, with five being the highest? Why?

10 Why did you choose this video to share?

> "Becoming number one is easier than remaining number one."
> —Bill Bradley (1943–), U.S. Senator; American Hall of Fame basketball player

 **Search & Share**   Reproducible

Exploring The Smithsonian

Student Name: _____ Date: _____

The Smithsonian Institution, made up of 19 American museums, attracts millions of visitors each year. 17 museums are in Washington, D.C. and two outside the nation's capital. The Smithsonian's museums showcase art and artifacts related to American history, natural history, culture, and science.

Select one Smithsonian museum from the Smithsonian Institution's official website: **www.si.edu.** After browsing their online collections, select an artwork or artifact from the exhibits, take notes, and share with your group.

Smithsonian Museum: _____

Location: _____

Title of artwork/artifact: _____

Artist/Attributed Culture: _____ Date and/or Period: _____

1 Describe the Smithsonian museum you chose.

2 Why did you choose this museum?

3 Which collection on display at this museum interests you the most? Why?

4 What kind of art and/or artifacts are featured in the collection?

5 Briefly describe the artwork or artifact you chose.

6 Why did you choose this artwork and/or object?

7 Is there a connection between the object/artwork and American history?

8 If you could own an artwork and/or artifact in the Smithsonian collection, which one would it be? Why?

9 Why do you think the Smithsonian Museums are so popular?

10 What would you like to see to in a future Smithsonian exhibit? Why?

> **"An investment in knowledge always pays the best interest."**
> —Benjamin Franklin (1706-1790), American author and statesman

Exploring Art at a Museum

Student Name: _____ Date: _____

Browsing art collections at a museum can lead to many exciting discoveries. Choose an art museum that you are curious about and browse its collection online. Then, select one piece from the collections, take notes, and answer the questions below. Be prepared to share your answers with your classmates.

Museum suggestions:

- The Metropolitan Museum of Art (New York, USA)
- The Getty Center (Los Angeles, USA)
- The Louvre (Paris, France)
- The Tate Modern (London, England)
- Museo del Prado (Madrid, Spain)

- The Uffizi Gallery (Florence, Italy)
- The Hermitage Museum (St. Petersburg, Russia)
- The National Palace Museum (Taipei, Taiwan)
- National Museum of China (Beijing, China)
- The National Art Center (Tokyo, Japan)

Title of artwork: _____

Artist: _____

Medium used: _____ Date: _____

1 Describe the museum you chose.

2 Have you ever visited the museum you chose? If not, why would you like to visit this museum?

3 Which collection on display at this museum interests you the most? Why?

4 Describe the artwork you chose. What is the subject matter?

5 What do you know about the artist?

6 Does the artist have other works on display at the museum? If so, what are they?

7   What do you like most about this piece of art?

8 What emotion(s) do you feel while looking at the artwork? Why? What about it makes you feel that way?

9 Would you put a poster of it on display in your home? Why or why not?

10 If you could ask the artist one question, what would it be?

> **"Art is not for the cultivated taste. It is to cultivate taste."**
> —Nikki Giovanni (1943-), American poet, author and lecturer

Watching the News

Student Name: _____ Date: _____

For homework, watch a news report in your best language for 5-10 minutes. You can use the TV or the Internet to find a video in which a news announcer is sitting in the studio presenting the news.

First watch the news with the sound "muted" or with the volume turned all the way down, so you can focus on the presenter's body language. As you watch, look at the speaker's mouth, face, hands, and body movements.

> Video (non-English): _____
>
> Source: _____ Topic: _____
>
> Topic/Gestures: _____

Next, find another 5-10 minute news report on TV or on the Internet (ex. CNN.com or BBC.com) in English. Like before, watch it with the volume as low as possible or on the "mute" setting. While you watch, again pay attention to the person's mouth, face, hands and gestures.

> Video (non-English): _____
>
> Source: _____ Topic: _____
>
> Topic/Gestures: _____

Describe the person speaking your best language or mother tongue. Describe the person speaking English. Was the mouth of either announcer open wide more often? What did you notice about the person's face or hands? What else did you see? What do you think this means?

> **"The body never lies."**
> —Martha Graham (1894–1991), American dancer and choreographer

Documenting Moments in Time

Student Name: _____ Date: _____

Documentary photographs capture important moments in time. Visit the **Library of Congress collection** to find a special historical photograph that captures your imagination. Print it out and share it with your classmates.

Title: _____

Photographer: _____

Historical Context: _____ Date: _____

1   Describe the photograph. What is going on?

2   Where was the photograph taken?

3   How did the photographer compose his picture? Where are your eyes drawn?

4   What historical moment does it capture? Does it do it well?

5   Why do you think the photographer chose to take this picture?

6   Why did you choose this photograph?

7   What did you learn from it?

8   Do you think a photograph like this would still be taken today? Why? Why not?

9   If a picture is worth a thousand words, what are five words that you associate with this photo?

     a

     b

     c

     d

     e

10   What do you look for when taking your own photographs? Why?

> "There are always two people in every picture: the photographer and the viewer."
> —Ansel Adams (1902–1984), American photographer and environmentalist

Chatting in Person and Online

Student Name: ———————————————————— Date: ————————————

Find an article about how friendship has changed since Facebook, Google+, and Twitter have become so popular. Do you think social media changes friendships? How so?
Read the article, print it out, and be prepared to discuss it with classmates.

Title: —————————————————————————————————————
Web address: ——————————————————————————————
Author: ———————————————————— Date: ————————————

1 Why did you chose this article to share with your classmates?

2 What's the main idea?

3 How many sources were quoted?

4 Were there any illustrations? What kind?

5 What did you learn from this article?

6 What was the most interesting part for you? Why?

7 Write five vocabulary words, idioms, or expressions related to this topic.

    a

    b

    c

    d

    e

8 How would you rate the article on a scale of 1-5, with five being the highest? Why?

9 What are your top tips for navigating social media?

10 What do you look for in your online friendships? Why?

> "Have friends. It's a second existence."
> —Baltasar Gracian (1601–1658), Spanish philosopher

1. HOW DO YOU SPEND YOUR TIME? (PG. 91)

How did you actually spend your time? Write a short reflective essay on differences between how you expected to spend your time and how you spent your time. Share with a close friend or relative.

2. SHARING MUSICAL TASTES (PG. 92)

What would like for your classmates to know about your favorite singer, musician, band, or group? Create a two to five-minute video review and share your musical tastes with your peers.

3. SHARING RESTAURANT RECOMMENDATIONS (PG. 93)

How do you start the day? Describe your favorite breakfast restaurant. Write a short Yelp recommendation for this restaurant and share on the class blog.

4. TV OR NOT TV (IS THAT A QUESTION?) (PG. 94)

What's your favorite TV show? Give a short recommendation and share it on the class blog. Provide relevant details.

5. ENJOYING A GREAT GAME (PG. 95)

Pretend you covered this great game as a sports journalist. Write your own commentary for the game, record yourself, and share your video on the class blog.

6. EXPLORING THE SMITHSONIAN (PG. 96)

Can you think of any ideas for a future museum exhibit? Pitch your idea for a future exhibit in a memo and share with the class.

7. EXPLORING ART AT A MUSEUM (PG. 97)

What would you ask the artist on display in an interview? Write a short, imaginary mock-interview of 5-10 questions between the artist and you.

8. WATCHING THE NEWS (PG. 98)

What is some news from your home country that you want to share? Report the news in English and another to report the news in a language other than English in a two to three-minute video. Share your video on the class blog!

9. DOCUMENTING MOMENTS IN TIME (PG. 99)

What are your favorite personal photographs? Choose three photographs that you would like to share with your classmates in small groups. Explain why you chose each photograph.

10. CHATTING IN PERSON AND ONLINE (PG. 100)

What are the pleasures and perils of using social media to make friends? What advice can you offer for happy and healthy online relationships? Share it on the class blog.

APPENDIX

Student Name: _____ Date: _____
Home Country: _____ Best Language: _____
Field: _____ Future Job Title: _____

1   Why do you want to speak better English? Give three reasons.

    a

    b

    c

2   How can speaking better English help you?

3   What activities or methods have you found most helpful in improving your English? Why?

4   What is the most helpful English class that you have had? Tell us more about that class.

5   What are some reasons some people sometimes dislike English class?

6   How else could speaking more fluent English change your life outside of school?

7   Can you list three topics that you would like to discuss with your classmates this semester?

    a

    b

    c

8   What are your strengths as an English language learner?

9   What are some challenges that you want to work on this semester?

10   What three things can you do this semester to improve your English?

Student Name: ——————————————— Date: ———————————————

1 What are three vague generalizations about the United States?

    a

    b

    c

2 What are some proverbs or slogans from your country or culture?

3 What are some popular songs that make universal claims?

4 Can you think of two sayings that contradict each other?

    a

    b

Note: Techniques for turning vague generalizations with more accurate, responsible statements:
- Add frequency adverb (sometimes, seldom, often)
- Weaken the verb (seem to, appear, tend to)
- Add modal (can, may, might,)
- Add qualifier (one of the best, an effective method)
- Identify conditions (when the information is known)
- Cite source (ex: "According to a 2013 WHO report...")

Activity 2:

Can you rewrite a generalization about Los Angeles?

Can you rephrase a traditional proverb or popular slogan?

SEEKING CLARIFICATION: KEY PHRASES

Checking what someone means:
- What do you mean by that? Do you mean...?
- In other words....?
- So are you saying...?
- Can you clarify that statement?
- Correct me if I'm wrong, but do you mean...?
- Sorry, I'm not sure if I got that. Are you saying...?

Asking someone to explain what they mean:
- Could you expand on that?
- Which means what?
- Which means what exactly? (more sceptical)
- What are the implications?
- Can you spin that out?
- Sorry, what exactly do you mean by that?
- Sorry, could you go over that again?

Checking that someone has understood you:
- Is that clear?
- Are you with me?
- Does that make everything clear?
- Can we move on?

Instructor Evaluation

Speaker:_____   Topic:_____
Time:_____   Date:_____

Indicate the extent to which you agree with the statement on the left, using a scale of 1-4 (**1=strongly disagree; 2=disagree; 3=agree; 4=strongly agree**). Total the numbers in each column.

Evaluation Criteria	Scale	Feedback
The presenter spoke **clearly**.		
The presenter spoke at an appropriate **volume**.		
The presenter spoke at a comfortable **pace**.		
The presenter **faced** the audience.		
The presenter stood up **straight and looked professional**.		
The presenter used effective **hand gestures**.		
The presenter made **eye contact** with the entire audience.		
The **introduction** caught my attention.		
The presenter provided some clear **examples**.		
The **conclusion** wrapped up the speech.		
The speaker effectively **answered questions**.		
Total:		

Short Answers:
What was good about this presentation?

What could have been better? What still needs to be improved?

Other observations and tips:

Two tips for the student presenter to do better on the next presentation.

  1._____
  2._____

Peer Response and a Question

Speaker:_____ Topic:_____

Time:_____ Date:_____

Short Answers:

1 What was good about this presentation? What worked?

2 What could they have done better? What still needs to be improved?

3 Other observations and tips:

_____

_____

_____

_____

_____

4 Write two tips for the student presenter to do better on the next presentation.

    a

    b

5 Ask a question to the speaker.

> "It's not that I'm so smart, it's just that I stay with problems longer."
> —Albert Einstein (1879–1955), American scientist

Speaker: _____   Topic: _____
Time: _____   Date: _____

Presentation Checklist

- o   Have I practiced many times?
- o   Did I get feedback from a classmate/friend?
- o   Have I timed my presentation (if applicable)?
- o   Do I introduce myself (if applicable)?
- o   Do I maintain eye contact?
- o   Do I explain my visuals (if applicable)?
- o   Do I pause sometimes and check for understanding?
- o   Did I look up words to correct my pronunciation?
- o   Am I using appropriate volume so that everyone can hear?

Self-evaluation

Indicate the extent to which you agree with the statement on the left, using a scale of 1-4 (**1=strongly disagree; 2=disagree; 3=agree; 4=strongly agree**). Total the numbers in each column.

Evaluation Criteria	Scale	Feedback
I spoke **clearly**.		
I spoke at an appropriate **volume**.		
I spoke at a comfortable **pace**.		
I **faced** the audience.		
I stood up **straight and looked professional**.		
I used effective hand **gestures**.		
I made **eye contact** with the entire audience.		
The **introduction** caught the audience's attention.		
I provided some clear **examples**.		
I **concluded** the speech in an effective way.		
I provided **solid answers** to questions.		
Total:		

What do you like about your presentation? What worked?

What could you have done better? What still needs to be improved?

Other observations and tips:

What are two things you will do differently in your next presentation?

Page 3

Recommended Link(s): National Public Radio, Inc. (NPR)
▶ https://www.npr.org/

Page 4

Recommended Link(s): "I Have a Dream..." Speech (via the National Archives)
▶ https://www.archives.gov/files/press/exhibits/dream-speech.pdf

Page 5

Recommended Link(s):
1) DOGO News
▶ https://www.dogonews.com/
2) Business Insider
▶ https://www.businessinsider.com/

Page 7

Recommended Link(s): Improving American English Pronunciation: Word stress
▶ https://www.youtube.com/watch?v=UPCxO-mJ8B0&feature=youtu.be

Page 8

Recommended Link(s): YouGlish
▶ https://youglish.com/

Page 21

Recommended Link(s): Understanding Your TOEFL iBT® Test Scores
▶ https://www.ets.org/toefl/ibt/scores/understand/

Page 28

Recommended Link(s): Airbnb
▶ https://www.airbnb.com/

Page 32

Recommended Link(s): Feline Conservation Center – Species Information
▶ http://www.cathouse-fcc.org/species.html

Page 33

Recommended Link(s): NPR Special Series: 'This I Believe'
▶ https://www.npr.org/series/4538138/this-i-believe

Page 42

Recommended Link(s): International Student Experience: Culture Shock
▶ Part 1: https://youtu.be/tPfB6GIjM9Q
▶ Part 2: https://youtu.be/H82IFq0HbTQ

Page 43

Recommended Link(s): True Happiness Test by Blue Zones ®
▶ https://apps.bluezones.com/en/happiness

Page 44

Recommended Link(s): TED: Ideas Worth Spreading
▶ https://www.ted.com/#/

Page 47

Recommended Link(s): Preparing for Natural Disasters
▶ https://www.ready.gov/be-informed
▶ https://www.epa.gov/natural-disasters
▶ https://www.redcross.org/get-help/how-to-prepare-for-emergencies/
types-of-emergencies.html

Page 48

Recommended Link(s): Do You Know How to Go Green? – National Geographic
▶ https://www.nationalgeographic.com/environment/global-warming/
green-lifestyle-quiz/

Page 59

Recommended Link(s): The Balance Careers
▶ https://www.thebalancecareers.com/

Page 60

Recommended Link(s):
1) Wired
   ▶ https://www.wired.com/
2) Popular Science
   ▶ https://www.popsci.com/

Page 66

Recommended Link(s): Make Money Choices – California Career Zone
   ▶ https://www.cacareerzone.org/budget/

Page 67

Recommended Link(s):
1) IMDb
   ▶ https://www.imdb.com/
2) Metacritic
   ▶ https://www.metacritic.com/

Page 69

Recommended Link(s): Discover Los Angeles
   ▶ https://www.discoverlosangeles.com/

Page 70

Recommended Link(s): Kelley Blue Book
   ▶ https://www.kbb.com/

Page 74

Recommended Link(s): Yelp
▶ https://www.yelp.com/

Page 81

Recommended Link(s): TripAdvisor
▶ https://www.tripadvisor.com/

Page 84

Recommended Link(s): Official Brazillian Tourism Website
▶ http://www.visitbrasil.com/en/

Page 86

Recommended Link(s): Japan National Tourism Organization
▶ https://us.jnto.go.jp/top/index.php

Page 87

Recommended Link(s): Vietnam National Administration of Tourism
▶ https://vietnam.travel/home

Page 94

Recommended Link(s): Full Episodes – NBC.com
  ▶ https://www.nbc.com/video

Page 95

Recommended Link(s):
1) ESPN
  ▶ http://www.espn.com/
2) Sports Illustrated
  ▶ https://www.si.com/

Page 96

Recommended Link(s): Smithsonian
  ▶ https://www.si.edu

Page 99

Recommended Link(s): Library of Congress Prints & Photographs Online Catalog
  ▶ http://www.loc.gov/pictures/

Online English as a Foreign Language (EFL) Resources to Keep Learning English

Accurate English
Lisa Mojsin helps professionals, actors, and adult students improve their English through accent reduction courses.
🌐 www.accurateenglish.com

Compelling Conversations
Visit our website to keep in touch, download free ESL/EFL work-sheets, and learn about more books for English Language learners.
🌐 www.CompellingConversations.com

English Daily
Links for ESL students to access English books, learning American Slang expressions, and English grammar lesson.
🌐 http://www.englishdaily626.com/

Randall's ESL Cyber Listening Lab
A deep, excellent resource for adult ESL students with developed listening exercises for low, intermediate, and high-intermediate students. Practical and impressive!
🌐 www.esl-lab.com

Free Rice
As students build their vocabulary, they are also helping end world hunger.
🌐 http://www.freerice.com

Guide to English Grammar and Writing
A valuable online collection of free tools, quizzes, and worksheets to help Community college students improve their grammar and writing skills.
🌐 www.grammar.ccc.commnet.edu/grammar

The Internet TESL Journal's Self-Study Quizzes for ESL Students
Self-study quizzes for ESL students including grammar and vocabulary quizzes.
Free games, quizzes, and puzzles that you can access online.
🌐 http://a4esl.org/q/h/

Learner's Dictionary
A free online dictionary designed to help ESL students understand new vocabulary words, featuring simple merriam-webster definitions and example sentences.
🌐 http://www.learnersdictionary.com/

Many Things
A rich resource for English language learners at multiple levels. The site includes vocabulary quizzes, proverb quizzes, and idiom games.
🌐 www.manythings.org

The Purdue Online Writing Lab (OWL)
Writing tips from Purdue University's acclaimed Online Writing Lab (OWL). Includes excellent ESL tips.
🌐 www.owl.english.purdue.edu/owl

TED Talks
Hear some of the world's leading experts speak about a wide variety of topics. Most talks are 15–20 minutes long, but you can start with the short talks of less than six minutes. Many videos include subtitles too.
🌐 www.ted.com

The Internet TESL Journal
Guide to English Grammar
Useful links such as tests, quizzes, listening, vocabulary, spelling, speaking, reading, and more.
🌐 http://iteslj.org/links/ESL/

This I Believe
This nonprofit educational website includes thousands of essays and podcasts about personal beliefs. It is widely used by American high school and college English departments to both encourage and showcase personal essays.
🌐 www.thisibelieve.com

USA Learns
This Sacramento County Office of Education website combines video lessons and clear written English for English language learners worldwide.
🌐 www.usalearns.org

Using English
Resources for learning the English language for ESL, EFL, ESOL, and EAP students and teachers. It has online tests and quizzes that are useful for ESL students.
🌐 http://www.usingenglish.com/

Voice of America
This wonderful public radio website is designed for English language learners. Short, slow radio reports look at American history, national parks, the English language, and current news.
🌐 www.voanews.com/learningenglish

YouGlish
Google created this powerful pronunciation tool for international English language learners. Visitors choose words and phrases, and the user hears them in authentic contexts in videos. Recommended for intermediate and advanced students.
🌐 www.YouGlish.com

> "All the world is my school and all humanity is my teacher."
> —George Whitman(1913-2011), Founder of Shakespeare and Company

Recommended Supplemental Apps

EasyBib is a tool that helps you create citations in MLA, APA and Chicago/Turabian styles. With EasyBib you can create a works cited list and parenthetical (in-text) citations. Great for research or advanced writing classes!

GrammarUp has different sections of the app, devoted to different parts of speech (e.g. adjectives, adverbs, causative verbs, and conditionals). Each section has the technical definition of the part of speech, followed by a practice test for students to take and practice.

Words with Friends is a multi-player word game, in which players take turns building words crossword puzzle-style, in a manner similar to the classic board game Scrabble. It helps develop spelling and build vocabulary by encouraging word formation.

Speak English such as you to listen to recordings of English speakers talking about a variety of topics, such as job interviews and customer service. After listening to it as many times as you'd like, you can then record yourself repeating the phrases.

FluentU offers language immersion through native videos. Their method allows you to learn words in context in a natural way because it takes real-world videos—like music videos, commercials, news, cartoons and inspiring talks—and turns them into English learning experiences.

Business Insider is an American business, celebrity, and technology news app that will keep students up on the latest news, so that they can easily converse with native English speakers.

TOEFL Go! is the only official TOEFL® app from ETS, the maker of the TOEFL® test.

Newsmart takes daily content from Wall Street Journal's articles and turns it into English lessons for English and Business English students. Each article is labeled by Learning Level. so students can read at their own level.

Eric H. Roth

teaches international graduate students the pleasures and perils of academic writing and public speaking in English at the University of Southern California (USC) as a Master Lecturer. He also consults with English language schools on communicative methods to effectively teach English.

Given a full scholarship as a Lilly Scholar, Roth studied philosophy and American history at Wabash College (1980-1984), and received his M.A. in Media Studies from the New School (1988). Since 1992, Roth has taught English to high school, community college, adult, and university students.

Highlights include teaching USC writing courses in Spain (2007) and Paris, France (2008); and directing the APU International High School in Ho Chi Minh City, Vietnam (2009). USC also awarded Roth two USC Teaching with Technology grants in 2012. He has also given several TESOL presentations since 2011, and has helped USC students applying for Fulbright positions as English Teaching Assistants (ETA) since 2012. Roth also served on the National Selection Committee for the Fullbright ETA program for Southeast Asia in 2015, 2016, and 2017.

Roth co-authored *Compelling Conversations: Questions and Quotations on Timeless Topics* in 2006 to help English language learners increase their English fluency. Recommended by English Teaching Professional magazine, this advanced ESL textbook has been used in over 50 countries in English classrooms and conversation clubs. Easy English Times, an adult literacy newspaper, has published a monthly column, "Instant Conversation Activities," based on the book since 2008. The first specific version for a particular country, Vietnam, was published in 2011. *Compelling American Conversations: Questions and Quotations for Intermediate American English Language Learners* appeared in 2012 and a Teacher Edition followed in 2015. *Compelling Conversations – Japan* came out in 2015. Roth and Nguyen coauthored an expanded, second edition of *Compelling Conversations – Vietnam: Speaking Exercises for Vietnamese Learners of English* in 2017.

A member of the USC faculty since 2003, Roth is also a member of numerous professional organizations including: California Association of Teaching English to Speakers of Other Languages (CATESOL); the International Communication Association (ICA); the International Professors Project (IPP); and Teaching English to Speakers of Other Languages (TESOL). Roth has given several CATESOL and TESOL conference presentations and led many teacher training worshops. He writes short reflective essays, reviews ESL/EFL related books and apps, and shares ELT teaching tips at CompellingConversations.com/blog.

Roth looks forward to learning something new today, tomorrow, and the day after tomorrow.

Teresa X. Nguyen

is a California-based content creator. She is the creator of ESL Garage, a bilingual (English-Vietnamese) YouTube channel for English language learners. She is the co-author of *Compelling Conversations – Vietnam* (2017), 60 Positive Activities for Every Classroom (2018), and 60 Positive Activities for Kids (2019). She is faculty at Golden West College located in surf-city Huntington Beach, California.

Her YouTube education projects, materials writing, and classrooms reflect over a decade of learning and teaching experience. The experiential basis for this communicative ESL textbook is her own struggles and successes as an international student studying abroad in Korea (2006), Spain (2007), and China (2008) as well as the depth and breath of her teaching experience. She has taught English language learners from over 25 countries in China, Vietnam, and the United States. Her students have included a wide range from elementary school pupils to graduate students.

An active member of several professional teaching organizations, Nguyen is co-president of the Material Writers Interest Group for TESOL. In addition, she has also presented at several English teacher conferences, including TESOL international conferences in Chicago, Illinois (2018), Seattle, Washington (2017), and Baltimore, Maryland (2016); CATESOL conferences in Anaheim, California (2018) & Santa Clara, California (2017); and On Course National Conference (2019). Her presentations focus on the optimal use of EdTech pedagogy and student mental health. However, Nguyen's most rewarding career experience – so far – has been supervising and training TESOL graduate students as a Master teacher (2013-2017).

A workaholic/workout-aholic by day and Korean-drama addict by night, she is a total travel and food junkie. You can connect with Teresa on Instagram and Facebook @eslgarage, or via her website, teresaxuanguyen.com.

Andrea Schmidt

is the design director and deputy editor for Chimayo Press. In addition to writing for and editing the Compelling Conversations blog, she has also worked on a variety of design projects for the company, including the cover of this book.

An alum of Otis College of Art and Design, Andrea completed a BFA in Communication Arts with a focus in Illustration. Her lifelong passion for writing and language also lead her to pursue a minor in Creative Writing.

A big believer in the power of open, honest communication, she was an original member of Team International Student Outreach (TISO) at Otis College. This initiative was created to help international students acclimate to their new surroundings while breaking down cultural barriers and promoting friendship without borders. To that end, TISO hosted many school-sponsored events, often with a cultural focus, to encourage a supportive campus community.

At her previous school, Harrisburg Area Community College (HACC), Andrea worked as a writing tutor. There she connected with many ESL students and helped them improve their written English skills, providing encouragement and support as needed. These experiences gave her new insight on the pleasures and perils of learning English, and ultimately became the basis for her interest in Chimayo Press.

Currently, Andrea is pursuing freelance illustration and design work in addition to her duties at Chimayo Press. She is also in the process of completing her TEFL certification through International TEFL Academy in the hopes of furthering her knowledge on English language instruction. Her future plans include building up her visual portfolio and applying to English teaching positions abroad in East Asia.

Toni Aberson

(M.A. English; M.A. Psychology and Religion) brings 35 years of teaching English and supervising English teachers to her materials writing. "The challenge for English teachers is to put our students at ease and encourage them to practice English," notes Aberson. "What better way than to ask students about their lives?

Aberson also co-wrote *Compelling Conversations: Questions and Quotations on Timeless Topics* (2007), and *Compelling American Conversations: Questions and Quotations for Intermediate American English Language English Language Learners* (2012). She also wrote *It's a Breeze: 42 Lively ESL Lessons on American Idioms* (2012) which focuses on common expressions used in everyday situations.

"I love teaching English," Aberson says. "The key in a classroom is engagement and people become interested and excited when they're learning about the daily stuff of life. When they are thinking and writing and talking about their real lives—food, jobs, family, homes, sports, movies— that's when they learn the language. Learning English is not easy. It can be a real challenge, but it can also be fun and stimulating. That's what I'm aiming for—the real life and the fun that stimulates immigrants and English students so they want to learn more. They want to jump in."

Hal Bogotch

Hal Bogotch has taught Adult ESL, Technology, and Literacy Skills for more than 15 years. Hal is also one of Chimayo Press's "go to" freelance editors and the co-author of *Compelling American Conversations: Questions and Quotations for High Intermediate English Language Learners.* His poetry can be found in the Free Venice Beachhead, Rattle, and other literary journals. Hal's wife, Laura Lacámara, is an award-winning children's book author/illustrator. They live together in Venice Beach, California.

Trinity Bustria

Trinity Bustria is an aspiring linguist, ESL teacher, and materials writer. The California-born educator majored in Liberal Arts (with a concentration in East Asian Religions and Languages) at the University of the West—a private, Buddhist-affiliated university—where he graduated as valedictorian and gave a commencement speech in 2019. Trinity intends to use his undergraduate studies as a foundation for graduate and doctoral studies in linguistics and religion.

Trinity's Korean and Chinese restaurant jobs have given him opportunities to employ language acquisition methods and techniques to learn some Korean and Mandarin. Additionally, he has taught English to Korean and Chinese elementary-high school students at a Korean-style cram-school.

Trinity is also a materials writer for Chimayo Press, an ELT educational publisher. His passion for language learning and teaching has enabled him to effectively assist international students from China, Taiwan, and Hong Kong develop and deepen their American English. He is currently conducting research for a publication on common, "good" mistakes committed by Chinese English-language learners.

Shiggy Ichinomiya

is a professional photographer, recreational triathelete, and English materials writer. After graduating from Boston University with a major in English, he moved to Japan, taught English to adults and children for a decade, and learned Japanese. These experiences informed his contributions to *Compelling Conversations – Japan: Questions and Quotations for High-Intermediate Japanese English Language Learners*, which he co-authored.

Yuka Kuroda

has taught and held administrative positions in the field of ESL/EFL. She is currently working as a Foreign Language Assistant in the public education system in France. Born in Southern California to Japanese parents, Kuroda grew up in a bilingual world. She quickly discovered her passion for literature and languages, and subsequently earned a bachelor's degree in comparative literature - with a minor in French - from UCLA.

Soon after completing her undergraduate education, she set her sights on becoming a social worker, and completed a fellowship in mental health. Through this experience, she learned that social work may not be her true calling, but also gained the realization that helping people and ameliorating the lives of others definitely was. Shortly after completing her fellowship, she began her graduate coursework in Education- TESOL at California State University- Fullerton, earning an M.S. in 2015.

As a graduate student, she worked as a Graduate Assistant in the English department, as well as a T.A. for an upper division Japanese course. She continuously strives to teach (and learn) language as a vehicle for communicating across cultures and as a tool to facilitate understanding and appreciation.

Tuanni B. Vasconcelos

currently works for Chimayo Press as a curriculum developer, marketing specialist, and research assistant. She possesses a Masters of Arts in Teaching – TESOL from the University of Southern California and she has over for years of experience teaching English and Portuguese as Second Languages, founding her own language school in Brazil in 2014. Currently, she is working on *Compelling Conversations – Brazil*, focused on helping Brazilian ESL students to develop their communication skills.

Brent Warner

Brent Warner is an assistant professor of ESL at Irvine Valley College in Orange County, California. Warner's work focuses on helping students move toward academic proficiency in college and university settings. He is an active volunteer and presenter in many professional development organizations, including CUE, CAP, and CATESOL. Warner is regularly asked to present on educational technology, skills integration, and best practices in the ESL classroom.

With a mind toward technology integration, Warner has been a pioneer in EdTech in ESL. He is the founder of EdTech.tv, a blog and podcast dedicated to education and technology.

About Chimayo Press

Sophisticated English for Global Souls

CHIMAYO PRESS is an independent educational publishing company committed to publishing niche books that create compelling conversations, deepen relationships, and celebrate the human spirit. We launched in 2005 with one advanced level English as a Second Language (ESL) title—Compelling Conversations: Questions and Quotations on Timeless Topics—from authors Eric H. Roth and Toni Aberson. This fluency-focused English textbook has blossomed into a series that meets the varying needs of English language learners and teachers in over 50 countries.

Compelling Conversations has also become the foundation for an expanding number of ESL and EFL (English as a Foreign Language) titles. The Compelling Conversations: Questions and Quotations series includes national versions for Vietnamese learners of American English (2011), American immigrants and refugees (2012), Japanese English language learners (2015). In 2012, we also published It's a Breeze: 42 Lively Lessons on American Idioms. In 2016, Compelling Conversations Vietnam - Speaking Exercises for Vietnamese Learners of English (Teresa X. Nguyen and Roth) took the series to a new level.

Janet Levine and Laurie Selik expanded the series to include professional books for native English speakers. Compelling Conversations for Fundraisers: Talk Your Way to Success with Donors and Funders (2016) continues the focus on building stronger relationships through better conversations. Future titles will include Compelling Conversations for Call Center Professionals and Compelling Conversations for Global Business Professionals.

As a small publisher, we are grateful for each purchase of our books. We have a growing list of both nonfiction and fiction titles—our authors include working English teachers, radio professionals, and screenwriters. Each distinctive book reflects the passion and perspectives of the authors. Visit www.ChimayoPress.com to see our growing catalog. English language teachers, tutors, and students are also invited to visit www.compellingconversations.com for more conversation materials and teacher tips.

Chimayo Press is named for our amazingly communicative, talented, and loving first border collie. We met Chimayo soon after a visit to the inspirational New Mexico town on a cross-country trip from Chicago to Los Angeles back in the 20th century. That's Chimayo's image in our logo. Would you like to review this book? We'd love to receive your feedback, read a positive review on Amazon, and start another new conversation!

Ask more. Know more. Share more.
Create Compelling Conversations.
🌐 www.CompellingConversations.com

Compelling Conversations

"In my own teaching, I have found questions and quotations to be highly effective in promoting student discussion. Questions are useful in that they require a response from the listener. Asking them also helps students master the tricky rules of the interrogative. Quotations are brilliant flashes of wit expressed in the shorest space possible, often just a sentence or two. The authors have compiled a formidable collection of quotations by famous people. The authors also add some wise proverbs here and there. My two favorites were 'Recite patience three times and it will spare you a murder' and 'When money talks, truth keeps silent,' which are from Korea and Russia. In sum, Compelling Conversations is a recommended resource for teachers who want to make their conversation classes more learner-centered. It should be especially appealing to those who wish to escape the confines of the Presentation-Practice-Production approach and do without a formal grammatical or functional syllabus. It reflects the authors' considerable professional experience, and would be a notable addition to any English teacher's bookshelf."

—Hall Houston English Teaching Professional magazine (January 2009)

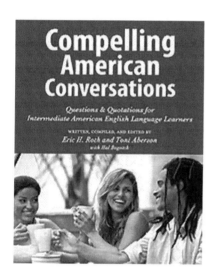

Compelling American Conversations

"How can so much learning be in just one book? Compelling American Conversations is all that an ESL teacher or student needs to use in their course. With clear, easyto- follow directions, students learn necessary details about American English and culture, practice critical thinking, and expand vocabulary and idioms as they converse in real, natural adult English. Included in the "Search and Share"component are marvelous lessons on using the Internet. An extra bonus is that any of the conversations, quotes, etc. can be used as writing prompts. The book is fun and stimulating and, fortunately, very accessible for the intermediate learner."

—Planaria Price, author of *Life in the USA*

Compelling Conversations - Japan

"As an ESL teacher and accent reduction coach, I regularly encounter frustrated students from Japan who don't feel comfortable speaking English. Compelling Conversations – Japan will prove very useful to Japanese English Language Learners ... It's more than just a conversation book; it's also a cross-cultural awareness book, filled with proverbs and cultural insights. In addition, it features valuable English pronunciation exercises focusing on the sounds that are difficult for native Japanese speakers. It also contains numerous fun and thought-provoking conversation topics relevant to a person from a Japanese cultural background."

—Lisa Mojsin, Author, *Mastering the American Accent*

Made in the USA
Middletown, DE
16 October 2023

40953967R00080